Doctor Robert Lefever

The Promis Re

common sense
in the treatment of

eating
disorders

PROMIS

Written by Dr Robert Lefever

PROMIS Recovery Centre Limited
The Old Court House, Pinners Hill
Nonington, Nr. Canterbury
Kent CT15 4LL. UK
www.promis.co.uk

ISBN 1 871013 17 8

Design and production by Rainbow, Ipswich IP5 3RY, England.
Printed in Basauri, Spain by Grafo SA.

Introduction

When Dr Robert Lefever asked me to introduce his latest book on eating disorders, my immediate thought was "Is he trying to tell me something?". Once I had been reassured, I thought "Why not?". In my work I come across a lot of people, often young and female (but not always), who are striving for the perfect body – whatever that is. Worse still, I am appalled when I see beautiful young kids, often barely out of primary school, ruining their lives trying to look like fashion models or pop star idols. Equally, on my travels, I can't help noticing the number of grossly overweight people I see on the streets of affluent Western countries. What are we doing to our children, our families and loved ones?

We all know friends or colleagues who are dieting and yet we may secretly wish we had their boobs, their bums or simply their body. Why? Until I read this book I admired their willpower. A friend would announce, "I've lost four pounds this week: all I've eaten since Christmas is grapefruit". "Aren't you clever", I would reply. Now I know better.

This book should be compulsive reading, not just for those with the extremes of eating disorders, but everyone – we can all learn from Dr Robert's experience and then learn to enjoy our food. The book should be in every school and children who think they are too fat or too thin should read this first ... and so should their parents, friends and teachers.

Pasty Palmer
'Bianca' in Eastenders

Dedication
To all those for whom one bite
is either too little or too much.

Acknowledgements

To my secretary, Sarah Oaten, for typing the manuscript,
to my editor Dr Harriet Harvey Wood for her expertise,
to my staff and patients for their encouragement and enthusiasm and
to Keith Burns for proof reading.

Contents

The means by which certain pleasures are gained
bring pains many times greater than the pleasures.

Epicurus

Chapter One

Fat Comes from Food

Avoiding Reality

However hard we try, we cannot avoid reality: fat comes from food. If we eat more than we require for energy and biochemistry, we put on weight. If we eat less than required, we lose it - and that is that: there is nothing more that can be said on that particular subject. If people want to lose weight they should eat less and take more exercise. If they need to put it on, as in anorexia, they should do the opposite. This may not seem to be a very friendly or sympathetic thing to say, but it is unquestionably the truth.

Of course there are medical conditions such as thyroid deficiency, diabetes, Cushing's syndrome, cardiac failure or kidney failure in which weight tends to increase and there are others, such as thyrotoxicosis, malabsorption syndromes and various infections and cancers in which one may lose weight. Obviously we need to seek medical advice if we have unexpected changes in body weight. However, we should ensure that we get genuine medical advice and proper clinical investigation, with blood tests and other analyses, and that we do not get taken in by "alternative" pseudo-science that talks of "glands", "fluid-retention" and "cellulite". If there is a problem with one's endocrine glands or with fluid retention it needs to be properly assessed and these conditions are very easily differentiated from simple obesity or, conversely, the result of starvation. "Cellulite" is simply body fat -nothing more or less - and body fat is fluid at normal body temperature. "Cellulite" is not a mysterious substance that inexplicably appears from nowhere: it is body fat that comes from overeating. Getting rid of it with liposuction or various cosmetic surgery operations will not solve the problem at all. If the overeating continues, then body fat will return and, call it what you like, it is still fat.

The concept of whether one is "fat" or "thin" is largely cultural. The photographic models of today would have been considered anorexic thirty years ago - and perhaps should be today. In some parts of the world, people whom we in the West would consider grossly obese might be considered in their own countries to be healthy (free from AIDS and other wasting diseases), powerful (rich enough to be able to afford to eat that much) and often beautiful. Even in the developed world the standard medical charts, giving "desirable" or "healthy" body weight for men or women of various heights, may not take sufficient account of normal healthy ranges in body weight in people of different body type (large, medium or small frame), body muscles (varying with the level of physical exercise performed during work or recreation) and age (we tend to shrink as we get older). Furthermore, many of these charts were drawn up at a time between the two world wars when the population was generally rather undernourished. In times that are more prosperous we may be heavier but we are not necessarily less healthy, nor do we necessarily have a shorter life expectancy simply because we come outside that particular "healthy" range.

The best way of judging whether we are physically healthy in terms of our body weight is to see how far or fast we can run comfortably. If, under retirement age, you can run two miles in twenty minutes without getting particularly out of breath or tired, then you probably don't have to worry too much about being overweight. If, on the other hand, you have an absolute need to run two miles or more as fast as you can in order to burn off as many calories as possible, then you may well have a problem at the anorexic end of the scale. If your body weight varies from year to year by over seven pounds up or down - or both up and down at different times - then you may well have an eating disorder, particularly where there is no other obvious medical or social reason for that change. You may also have an eating disorder if you control your body weight by alternately bingeing and starving, by exercising excessively or by vomiting or purging.

Similarly, if your exercise level changes dramatically from year to year other than in response to a specific medical or social change, then again an eating disorder (in the form of the commonly associated exercise addiction) may be a possible cause.

That being said, the vast majority of people who are on diets at any one time do not have eating disorders and do not have any significant medical condition. They are simply trying to change the way they feel by changing the way they look to themselves and, by inference, to other people.

Telling a classroom of sixteen-year-old girls that putting on four or five pounds in weight will probably not be of any medical importance whatever would be likely to be greeted with derision. They would ask what planet you came from. For them, an increase in body weight of four or five pounds would be considered to be an utter disaster and it is unthinkable that it could be considered to be medically irrelevant. These are normal perceptions in normal sixteen-year-old girls: a great deal of their self-image is centred upon their physical appearance, as interpreted by themselves and within their socio-cultural group. Young men might have equally fixed impressions on the importance of muscularity. They may play sports in order to demonstrate not only their physical fitness but also their attractiveness. If only human relationships were so simple!

It would be nice to believe that we would grow out of these false perceptions when we are no longer teenagers - but we don't. Many women retain an admiration for the "androgynous" body shape, resembling that of men. They may hate their breasts, bellies and thighs precisely because they look like the breasts, bellies and thighs of women. The distribution of their body fat is under direct control of ovarian hormones (or, to be scientifically precise, to the absence of male hormones). Correspondingly, men tend to go haring off to the gymnasium as soon as they suffer an emotional crisis such as discovering that their wives have been unfaithful to them. In each case our self-perception is very much tied up with our body weight and shape.

It is this self-perception, so intricately bound up with our emotional lives, that results in the diet industry being so massive. The very fact that slimming magazines can survive beyond their first and second issues is manifest proof that their advice does not work. Yet week after week new "special" diets are peddled to the gullible. Totally crazy notions on the timing of food intake or on the combination of different foods or on particular inclusion or exclusion diets, somehow survive the test of time and disillusion. People who fail to adhere to the regime tend to blame themselves rather than the stupid notions. The plain fact is that any dietary regime can be designed to take off weight or put it on but eventually the only way to maintain one's body weight is to balance calorie intake and calorie output, taking in only the quantity of food that one needs in order to generate sufficient calories for energy and biochemistry. That is not exactly rocket science: it simply says that fat comes from food.

Counting calories can become an obsession and is very much part of the anorexic mind-set. Some knowledge of the calorie content of various foodstuffs is sensible. For example four ounces of lamb would be five hundred and seventy calories whereas four ounces of boiled potatoes would be only eighty calories. People often imagine that it is the potatoes rather than the meat that is fattening. Sensible education on approximate calorie intake is therefore appropriate - but counting every one, or even every ten or twenty or fifty, is daft and is a common feature of people who suffer from eating disorders.

Crash diets tend to set up cravings and also produce a sense of deprivation. The more one starves, the more one wants to eat, and the more one feels one deserves to do so. However, studies of shipwrecked mariners or of people who have been deliberately starved under laboratory observation show that a line is crossed beyond which the mind starts telling lies and true perceptions are distorted. Anorexia nervosa itself is probably a genetically inherited defect in the neurotransmission (brain biochemistry) systems in the mood centres of the brain and is similar to other compulsive disorders such as alcoholism and drug addiction. However, any one of us can develop a temporary anorexic mind-set by crash dieting just as we can get temporarily drunk or stoned through the use of alcohol or drugs. Crash diets are therefore not a good idea: they can be dangerous as well as ineffective.

Most commonly crash diets are followed by rebound binges and then the whole cycle begins all over again. The best way of losing weight is to do so gradually, for example on a 1,000-calorie-a-day diet, including plenty of highly nutritious, low calorie, bulk foods such as various varieties of bean. The protein content of beans provides the nutritional balance, low-calorie content helps one to lose weight and the bulk reduces hunger and still there is room to add an egg or some fish, and then have some fresh fruit so as to provide variety of taste and a bit of pleasure as well as satisfying one's daily nutritional requirements. On a total of 1,000 calories a day, one should lose 4 lbs of weight a week provided that one takes a bit of exercise and is not totally sedentary.

The other way to lose weight comfortably is to increase the amount of exercise one takes. A brisk walk for twenty minutes a day will burn off excess calories and stimulate body biochemistry so that it works at a higher level of activity.

For a normal healthy diet one should not need the advice of a dietician. Anorexic patients should certainly not turn to dieticians for advice. They need no specific dietary advice other than to eat normally. By becoming obsessed with dietetics, they take themselves further away from normality. The proper function of dieticians is to help people who have diabetes or kidney failure or other medical conditions that require special diets. Anorexia does not require special diets other than inital vitamin supplements and high calorie drinks. Otherwise it requires a normal diet.

The concept of "health foods" is bizarre. There is in fact nothing particularly unhealthy about "junk" food if it is eaten occasionally rather than exclusively. To reject it on the grounds that it does not taste very special is fair enough, but to attack it on the grounds of nutritional inadequacy shows very little understanding of the actual needs of the stomach and body in general. By and large, vitamins, minerals and trace elements have very little to do with health except in absolute deficiency states which are clinically rare. Premature babies, isolated old ladies, prisoners of war or vegan diet fanatics may have a problem but the rest of us do perfectly well even if our diets occasionally contain various forms of "junk" food. In any case, if people are so worried about their health, they should focus primarily upon stopping smoking cigarettes. "Junk" food would, by comparison, be a very long way down the list of appropriate concerns.

The issue of "junk" food tends to be a political one, just as concerns for the "environment" are often also politically motivated. In both cases the attack is primarily upon globalisation and there is little or no evidence to support the belief that damage is caused in the particular ways that are the subject of concern. It is true that poverty and malnutrition are serious and widespread problems, just as it is true that there is widespread environmental damage but, as Bjorn Lomborg demonstrates conclusively with a wide range of scientific evidence in his book *The Skeptical Environmentalist* (Cambridge, 2001), the true causes of nutritional and environmental damage are far from what they are commonly made out to be. Education has to be distinguished from propaganda.

The solution to problems of diet, nutrition and body weight in normal society is primarily to eat a normal, healthy, mixed diet, with three regular meals a day and no snacks in between. Spreading one's food intake to include fats, carbohydrates and proteins is essential. One should have whole grains, nuts, fish and white meat in preference to red, and one should have plenty of fresh fruit and vegetables. That is really all one needs to know. There is no place for supplements and there is absolutely no place for pharmacological substances to stimulate or reduce the appetite. These substances will inevitably be addictive when they are used in an attempt to influence an emotional problem (an eating disorder as such or, alternatively, simple comfort eating, comfort starving or - believe it or not - comfort vomiting or purging) by treating the end results rather than looking at the cause.

Ultimately we should learn to eat according to hunger. Most people do that anyway although they may occasionally have a pork-out or put themselves temporarily on a diet to lose a few pounds for some reason best known to them. For people with eating disorders, however, the idea of eating according to hunger is novel. They would tend to eat or abstain when they are angry, lonely or tired rather than when they are hungry or full. For them the concept that fat comes from food is far from being a statement of the obvious: it is a fundamental challenge to their personal philosophy.

Chapter Two
Body Dysmorphia

Body dysmorphia is the state in which we do not believe that our body looks like what it actually does look like. We may see ourselves as fat when in fact we are thin - or vice versa - or we may believe that we have a particular blemish or major defect when other people would hardly notice it, if at all.

Body dysmorphia is a state of mind, a perception deficit and, as such, is exceedingly difficult to treat. A basic feature of any addictive or compulsive behaviour is the psychopathology of denial: the sufferer does not believe that he or she has the problem in the first place and therefore sees absolutely no reason why it should be treated. This is as true of eating disorders as it is of alcoholism or drug addiction or any other addictive or compulsive behaviour. Patients with eating disorders commonly also have body dysmorphic symptoms: they do not see themselves as others see them and a feature that totally obsesses them is heard with total incredulity by other people. Thus, for people suffering from eating disorders, there is commonly the dual difficulty of being told that one has something that one does not believe one has, and also believing that one has got something when other people say one has not. One way or another, other people's viewpoints come to be totally distrusted.

Perhaps we all have body dysmorphia to some slight degree. To be totally happy with one's shape and appearance, warts and all, is probably quite rare and is a sign of considerable maturity. To be just a bit uncomfortable - perhaps about the shape of the nose, or the straightness or thinning of the hair, or the presence of a paunch or of big buttocks or of bags under the eyes, or "poor" posture - is perfectly normal. It is only when it becomes an obsession - so that the attention given to it takes away from the natural easy enjoyment of life - that it becomes true body dysmorphia.

For some people body dysmorphic symptoms become so severe that they are utterly crippling. These people are absolutely convinced that a particular defect not only exists - when in other people's view it might not - but that it is such a terrible defect that it absolutely must be changed at all costs. They may try to hide it behind cosmetics or wear clothes to cover it or have plastic surgery to change it, but even then they may fail to be satisfied because the problem is actually in the mind, not in the body.

For precisely this reason, treatment has to be directed at the mind rather than at the body. Surgical treatment is a disaster. It can never achieve the change in perception that the patient needs. All it can change is the surgeon's view of the body, not the patient's. The result of surgery will always be a disappointment to these patients: it can never be exactly right. Even "before and after" photographs will be unconvincing to the patient. The problem will remain in the mind, regardless of what happened to the body. This principle is obvious and yet still physicians and surgeons, with the approval of psychiatrists, sometimes do extraordinarily inappropriate things to the body without understanding that these cannot change the mind. Pharmaceutical drugs such as anti-depressants are often prescribed in the hope that the patient will be better able to resolve emotional issues. In the short term the patient may indeed feel better, but the solution to the underlying problem will become even more elusive, now with the added complication of the patient's belief that there will be a pill for every ill.

In the longer term the patient becomes dependent upon the medication; anti-depressants are addictive even though they are slow to act and slow to produce withdrawal effects. Doctors are becoming progressively more aware of the addictive nature of anti-depressants, which, paradoxically, is precisely why they now frequently recommend that these drugs should be taken for life. But the elevation of mood will only be temporary, so the dosage will in due course need to be increased, or one drug changed for another, if the effectiveness is to remain the same - just as in any form of drug addiction. Furthermore, variation of mood is precisely what gives life its colour and to homogenise it with anti-depressants is a terrible thing to do to people. A life without colour may be functional but it has surely lost much of its value.

Surgeons may well be anxious to help their patients in any way they can but their methods are sometimes barbaric. Just as the treatment of alcoholism with Antabuse (which has a deterrent effect because it causes nausea when the patient drinks alcohol) and the treatment of drug addiction with Naltrexone (which is an anti-euphoriant, taking away the pleasure from the use of the drug) still leave the patients with underlying emotional cravings, similarly the use of surgical treatments such as jaw-wiring, stomach-stapling, intestinal shortening, liposuction and apronectomies, all leave sufferers from eating disorders with their continuing cravings. These treatments are not treatments at all: they merely tidy up the end result of the illness and do nothing whatever for the emotional illness itself. The cravings and the misery continue and the patient feels even more hopeless when yet another "treatment" fails. The surgeon may claim success, pointing to a change in body weight, but even their physician colleagues will point to the secondary effects of some of these procedures, affecting the liver and kidneys and other parts of the body as a result of changes in the absorption of nutrients from the gut. Even the surgeons themselves will become aware that their "treatments" often have to be repeated.

Paradoxically, the patients express gratitude to those who are in fact responsible for perpetuating their torment. They thank the physicians, psychiatrists and surgeons because they know that they were well intentioned - and often they were doing what the patients themselves most fervently requested - but they may, one and all, be deluded in believing that these "treatments" could ever work. They simply *cannot*: the problem is in the mind and the mind must be helped, not drugged or confused by allowing consequence to be separated from cause.

Successful treatment of body dysmorphia has to be directed towards the perception defect itself. As with alcoholism, drug addiction and other addictive or compulsive behaviours, the perception defect is the central psychopathology: the damaging behaviour is secondary. We have to work to change the "why" of the illness rather than the "what" or "how much" or "when". This principle shows the fallacy of "sensible drinking" programmes for alcoholism and "harm-minimisation" programmes for addiction. Correspondingly, the treatment of patients suffering from eating disorders has to look behind the "what" and "when" and "how often" to the "why". The "why" of body dysmorphia is generally as much misunderstood as the "why" of truancy. Children who run away from school are often not running away from something - such as bullying - but running towards something else. Some of them may be running away from unpleasant circumstances in school but all of them will be running towards a feeling of safety or a sense of need to do something (such as helping to protect mother) that is considered more important than staying at school.

On this same principle, patients with body dysmorphia are not running away from a bad image but trying to run towards a sense of perfection. Seen in this light, it is obvious that perfection can never be achieved through pharmaceutical or surgical intervention: the treatment has to be psychological. However, even psychological treatments can be misguided. Currently the form of psychotherapy favoured by most doctors tends to be cognitive-behavioural. In this approach the doctor or therapist calmly explains to the patient what he or she has misconceived and tells him or her what would be better. It sounds sensible and it flatters doctors and therapists who think that they always know the answers. However, for exactly those reasons, it can be patronising and ultimately totally ineffectual. One cannot treat an irrational problem with reason: it would not be an irrational problem if one could. The solution is to get inside the patient's madness, not to try to reason with it. I believe that the only people who can do this are those who have been there themselves: other people who have had the same problem and come through it. When the blind lead the blind they understand each other's difficulties: when the sighted lead the blind there is an inevitable divisive gulf between them.

Successful treatment of body dysmorphia comes from the awareness that one is not alone. In a group of similar sufferers one can see the distortions of other people's thinking and hence deduce one's own. This is the exact principle that underlies Alcoholics Anonymous and all the Anonymous Fellowships, including Overeaters Anonymous, Bulimics Anonymous and Anorexics Anonymous. Individual sufferers see themselves reflected in the mirror of the group and, by working the Twelve Step programme of recovery, gradually help themselves from the inside to change their perceptions and, as a result, change their behaviour.

Chapter Three
Food Obsession

To change an obsession for doing something into an obsession for not doing it is to change nothing at all that is worth changing. The essential first step in the understanding and treatment of eating disorders is to recognise that the problem lies primarily in the individual sufferer, not solely in the food itself. The problem is essentially the perception defect and mood disorder. This is exactly the same problem as in patients suffering from alcoholism, drug addiction, or any other addictive or compulsive behaviour. The problem goes with them, wherever they go and whatever they do. These people have what I believe is a neurotransmission defect in the mood centres of their brains. There may be a chemical defect in the way one nerve cell communicates with another. This leads to a mood disorder and the sufferers discover the mood-altering properties of alcohol, nicotine, cannabis or cocaine or other substances; or they may discover gambling or exercise or shopping and spending or other mood-altering behaviours.

Sufferers from eating disorders discover the mood-altering properties of sugar and white (refined) flour. The process of refinement takes away the fibre that provides the bulk of the vegetable and produces a mood-altering drug. Patients with neurotransmission disease discover for themselves that potatoes and rhubarb do not "work" in changing the mood whereas alcohol, caffeine, nicotine, cannabis, sugar and white flour all do. People who do not have neurotransmission defects drink alcohol for the taste, they smoke cigarettes - limited numbers in order to look "grown-up" - and they use cannabis and other recreational drugs in order to be daring or to feel part of the group. People who have neurotransmission disease use these substances in order to survive, in order to relieve their deep inner emptiness and suicidal depression. This is precisely why it is so difficult for them to give up these substances - because they dread going back to the absolute abyss that they were in before. It is small wonder that the Samaritans say that 40% of all suicides are in alcoholics alone. These people have got to the state where they can no longer live with the substance - because it has caused so many problems in their lives - but they also cannot contemplate living without it. Other people can never understand that - any more than they could understand, other than intellectually, what the world looks like to someone who is colour blind.

Correspondingly, sufferers from neurotransmission disease who discover the mood-altering effects of sugar and white flour will understand each other but generally not be understood at all by people who do not have the same or similar neurotransmission defects. An addict of one kind or another will generally understand the addictive process so that an alcoholic will understand a compulsive gambler, or a drug addict understand someone with an eating disorder, but someone who has no addictive tendency in his or her fundamental nature will never understand any of them from the inside.

There will of course be some misunderstandings between sufferers from neurotransmission disease of different kinds. Alcoholics will sometimes say that people who have eating disorders have a more difficult problem because they have to eat whereas they themselves can live without alcohol. The truth is that the only substances that need to be avoided in each case, are those that have a mood-altering effect: people with eating disorders have to abstain from sugar and white flour but can eat anything else and, correspondingly, alcoholics have to abstain from anything that contains alcohol but they can - and indeed have to - drink other things such as water or milk or orange juice because otherwise they could not survive any more than someone with an eating disorder could survive totally without food.

An obsession is not a habit. Habits can be broken: one can recognise that they are silly or self-destructive and train oneself to stop them. After a time they simply fade away. Obsessions are altogether different: they dominate the soul and every aspect of life. One cannot live without them: they are the starting position of each and every day. They are the central identity of the sufferer's life. They are not accessible either to reason or to kind words and gentle support. They are progressive and utterly destructive. In this way the difference between sadness and depression is all the difference in the world. Sadness is something that can happen to anybody as a result of unfortunate events. Depression has no explanation and is a profound chasm from which there is no escape. This is the inner emptiness of sufferers from neurotransmission disease. Depression and neurotransmission disease or addiction in any of its forms is all the same thing, before and after various attempts at self-medication. There is no escape from them. Obsessions would not be obsessions if there were an escape. Willpower and self-control, determination and moral fibre - whatever that may be - are all totally ineffective in the treatment of obsessions. In fact they make matters worse by reducing the self-esteem and self-confidence of the sufferers when these methods fail.

Ultimately the solution comes through surrender rather than permanent warfare. This was the essential paradox discovered by the co-founders of Alcoholics Anonymous: they could not help themselves other than through helping each other. The disease of utter isolation was treated with fellowship. Initially this may sound wet and weedy or even bizarre and supernatural - but it works. The paradox "I could not help myself until I realised that I could not help myself" becomes explicable when the emphasis is placed on the third "I": sufferers need the help of each other if they are to get their disease into remission, one day at a time, on a continuing basis.

Those who do not get their neurotransmission disease into recovery on a continuing basis tend to find another outlet for it. They remain obsessed in one way or another. People who have problems with drug addiction tend to have similar compulsive relationships in the use of alcohol, nicotine, caffeine, gambling and risk-taking and sexual activity. People who have eating disorders commonly also have addictive tendencies in their relationships with work, exercise, shopping and spending. At PROMIS we term the first group of addictions the "hedonistic" group and the second group "nurturant of self". It may be that each of these groups is related to a specific gene. It is doubtful whether there will be one gene for alcohol and another for cocaine or sugar or nicotine. It is, however, quite possible that there will be one genetic influence towards hedonism: "eat, drink and be merry for tomorrow we die!" and another towards nurturance of self: "I do this to make myself feel better and comfort myself". Some people may have one of these genetic tendencies or the other. Some may have both. A third genetic predisposition may lead towards compulsive helping (using oneself as a drug for other people) or, alternatively or additionally, relationship addiction (using other people as if they were drugs). Again this is sometimes seen on its own but at other times in combination with one or the other or both of the former hedonistic or nurturant addictive tendencies. Certainly these addictive tendencies tend to run in families, as often seen in epidemiological studies, so it will be no surprise if specific genes are discovered that influence the development of neurotransmission disease and hence addictive or compulsive behaviour in one or another of its outlets - provided that the researchers look in the right place for genes determining a general attitude rather than a specific compulsive behaviour.

Seen in this light, eating disorders are clearly part of the compulsive/addictive spectrum and have nothing in common with general psychiatric illness such as schizophrenia or manic depression (although alcoholism is often misdiagnosed as manic depression because of the extreme mood swings). Psychiatric approaches that focus solely upon changes of body weight and shape miss the point entirely in the treatment of eating disorders. A sufferer may move from starving to bingeing or discover vomiting and purging and hence not change the compulsive or addictive process at all even though the body weight may change, sometimes significantly, or alternatively stay static. Successful treatment does not begin until the entire obsessive process is confronted. Moving from one obsession to another, or changing specific behaviours within a general obsession, changes nothing. When someone suffering from an eating disorder moves across to shopping or spending or work or exercise, there is no genuine improvement: he or she is still obsessed and still behaving addictively and compulsively. When he or she changes from starving to bingeing or vomiting or purging there is still no change: nothing is genuinely achieved, irrespective of the change in weight, body shape or appearance. A determined attempt to control feelings by the use of food in one way or another will still be there and the whole complex set of obsessive beliefs and behaviours will ultimately show themselves again with destructive force.

This process can be seen when patients suffering from eating disorders become obsessed over health foods and vitamins, food allergies, irritable bowel syndrome, intestinal yeast infection with candida and post-viral fatigue syndrome (M.E.). The obsessions have not gone away: they have simply found other focuses of attention. The determination with which sufferers from eating disorders cling to these alternative diagnoses has to be seen to be believed. The parallel is with alcoholics who are determined to prove that their problems lie in their homes or at work or in the chemicals used in the making of wine or in anything other than in their own cravings for alcohol. Correspondingly, drug addicts will try to convince themselves and other people that some drugs are "soft" or "hard" and that they are perfectly functional when taking Methadone (an oral substitute for heroin, which is just as addictive as heroin, has double the mortality risks and singularly fails to do what it is intended to do – which is to keep people off heroin).

One way or another, sufferers from neurotransmission disease in all its various forms kid themselves and bamboozle other people - except other addicts. Obsessions are easy to understand when you yourself have got one. Food obsessions, and the various escape routes that enable the sufferer to look at anything and everything else other than self, are no different from any other form of obsession. They are just as all-pervasive, just as destructive and just as exasperating to the sufferers and to everyone else.

eating disorders

18

Chapter Four

Diagnosis

It is extremely important to be accurate in making the diagnosis of an eating disorder. To under-diagnose, missing the diagnosis when it should have been made, means that the illness will be perpetuated and more damage will be done whereas, hopefully, it could have been avoided. To over-diagnose, giving someone a diagnosis of having an eating disorder when in fact he or she does not, means that unnecessary treatment will have been given - causing considerable confusion in the mind of the patient - and perhaps a more appropriate diagnosis might have been missed. Questions therefore have to be framed specifically to delineate patients who have an eating disorder from people in the normal population. A question has no diagnostic value unless it represents a feature that would be found in patients suffering from an eating disorder and *only* in those patients rather than in the general population.

Consider the following absurd five-question Sick Control One Fat Food (SCOFF) questionnaire, which was designed to diagnose eating disorders. I assume that the purpose of this simple questionnaire was similar to the four-question CAGE questionnaire for the diagnosis of alcoholism. However, while simplicity is admirable, it may, as in the case of the SCOFF questionnaire, be totally misleading. Consider each of the questions in turn:

- *Do you make yourself **sick** because you feel uncomfortably full?*

   The first question would be insufficient to weed out young girls under emotional stress. During school examination years a lot of girls self-induce vomiting but subsequently have no evidence of an on-going eating disorder.

- *Do you worry you have lost **control** over how much you eat?*

   Patients with compulsive disorders tend to believe that they are still in control, however much other people may point out the contrary.

- *Have you recently lost more than **one** stone in a three-month period?*

   In addition to the obvious concern that one would express over thyrotoxicosis or carcinoma of the stomach and other significant ailments, there are people who go on diets simply because they have become rather flabby over the years rather than because they are compulsive overeaters or anorexic.

- *Do you believe yourself to be **fat** when others say you are too thin?*

   A large number of people have body dysmorphic symptoms to some slight degree. To include these patients in those suffering from eating disorders would be comparable to calling frequent visitors to the student bar alcoholics.

- *Would you say **food** dominates your life?*

   Someone who has an eating disorder may well cross-addict into work or exercise or shopping and spending and therefore temporarily be able to answer that food does *not* dominate his or her life at that time.

Without doubt these questions have the intention of being helpful to doctors in making an appropriate diagnosis (I read them in an issue of *General Practitioner* magazine) but I believe that they muddy the waters rather than clear them.

By contrast, the PROMIS Questionnaires on sixteen different outlets for addictive or compulsive behaviour, were based upon specific addictive characteristics as follows:

1. Preoccupation with use or non-use.

2. Preference for, or contentment with, use alone.

3. Use as a medicine to relax, sedate or stimulate.

4. Use primarily for mood-altering effect.

5. The tendency to protect supply, preferring to spend time, energy or money in this way.

6. Using more than planned, in that the first use tends to trigger the next.

7. Having a higher capacity than others for using the substance or behaviour without obvious damaging effect.

8. Continuing to use despite damage.

9. Having a tendency to cross-addict into other addictive substances or processes.

10. "Drug"-seeking behaviour, looking for opportunities to use, and progressively rejecting activities that preclude such opportunities.

11. "Drug"-dependent behaviour, "needing" the addictive substances or behaviour in order to function effectively.

12. Continuing to use despite the repeated serious concern of other people.

The PROMIS Questionnaires for bingeing and starving are as follows:

Each of these statements should be answered on a scale of 0 - 5 as follows:

5 = like me,
0 = not like me
1, 2, 3 or 4 = in between

Food bingeing

A total of twenty points indicates the need for further assessment.

1. I have tended to think of food not so much as a satisfier of hunger but as a reward for all the stress I endure.

2. I have tended to use food as both a comfort and strength even when I have not been hungry.

3. I have found that being full has often been irrelevant in deciding when to stop eating.

4. I have found that I have sometimes put on weight even when I am trying to diet.

5. Other people have expressed repeated serious concern about my excessive eating.

6. I have often preferred to eat alone rather than in company.

7. When I have definitely eaten too much I have tended to feel defiant as well as disappointed in myself.

8. I have preferred to graze like a cow throughout the day rather than ever allow myself to get hungry.

9. I have had three or more different sizes of clothes in my adult (non-pregnant if female) wardrobe.

10. I have been aware that once I have consumed certain foods I have found it difficult to control further eating.

Food starving

A total of twenty points indicates the need for further assessment.

1. In a restaurant or even at home I have often tried to persuade others to choose dishes that I knew I would like, even though I would probably refuse to eat them.

2. When I have eaten in company I have liked to be with special friends or family members whom I can rely upon to finish off some foods for me.

3. I have had a list of so many things that I dare not eat that there has been very little left that I can eat.

4. I have often chewed something (apart from gum) and then taken it out of my mouth and thrown it away.

5. I have particularly enjoyed eating raw vegetables and also salty or sour things.

6. When I have eaten in company I have tended to time my eating as a form of strategy so that others are not really aware of just how little I am eating.

7. When I have eaten something reasonably substantial I have tended to feel disappointed or even angry with myself as well as slightly relieved.

8. I have become irritable and impatient at meal times if someone has tried to persuade me to eat something.

9 I have often avoided meal times by claiming that I have already eaten when it is not true.

10. Some food has made me wish I could eat it as other people do but I have nonetheless found that I could not bring myself to do so.

The original PROMIS questionnaire had thirty questions on each addictive outlet, mostly focusing upon the first eight of these twelve addictive characteristics. It was found in practice to be time-consuming and cumbersome and was therefore cut down to one third of its length by selecting those answers that most commonly featured in patients with these specific addictive outlets. The questionnaires were validated against all the other addiction questionnaires commonly used throughout the world in various forms of addictive or compulsive behaviour and they were also validated against normal controls selected from my general medical practice and from psychology students. Over four thousand patients have now completed the Shorter PROMIS Questionnaires and it is available on our website (www.promis.co.uk) together with an automated scoring system to provide an insight into the significance of the answers. In general a total of twenty points on any individual outlet gives cause for concern.

For patients with eating disorders it is necessary to differentiate the two extremes of behaviour: bingeing and starving. There are therefore two questionnaires: one for each of these behaviours. Some patients will provide answers that are currently in one extreme or the other but it is common to find patients - as one would expect from clinical experience - who have both tendencies and who perhaps alternate from one to the other at different times in their lives. It is this specific awareness that illustrates that changing a patient's body weight is not necessarily an indication that his or her eating disorder has been treated successfully. A particular patient may move from starving to bingeing and go straight through what would be considered to be a normal body weight and finish up significantly the far side. Or perhaps a patient will discover that self-induced vomiting or purging can maintain body weight while he or she continues to have periodic or regular binges.

Patients who have eating disorders commonly cross-addict into work, exercise, shopping and spending. The specific characteristics that refer to these behaviours when they are addictive or compulsive are as follows:

As before, statements should be answered on a scale of 0 - 5 as follows:

$$5 = \text{like me,}$$
$$0 = \text{not like me}$$
$$1, 2, 3 \text{ or } 4 = \text{in between}$$

A total score of twenty points on each addictive outlet gives cause for concern.

Work
"Work" includes hobbies and interests, cults or sects.

1. I have taken on work that I actively disliked, not so much out of necessity but more simply to keep myself occupied.

2. I have tended to work faster and for longer hours than other people of my own ability so that they have found it difficult to keep up with me.

3. When I have definitely overworked and got myself irritable and over-tired, I have tended to feel defiant as well as slightly ashamed.

4. I have tended to tidy up the mess that someone else has got into at work, even when I have not been asked to do so.

5. I have found that finishing a specific project is often irrelevant in deciding when to stop working.

6. When working with others I have tended to disguise the full amount of time and effort that I put into my work.

7. I have tended to keep reserve projects up my sleeve just in case I find some time, even a few minutes, to spare.

8. I have regularly covered other people's work and responsibilities even when there was no need for me to do so.

9. Other people have expressed repeated serious concern over the amount of time I spend working.

10. I have found that once I start work in any day it has been difficult to get "out of the swing of it" and relax.

Exercise
1. I have often been so tired with exercise that I have found it difficult to walk or to climb up stairs.

2. I have preferred to exercise alone rather than in company.

3. I have often tried to take exercise several times a day.

4. I have particularly enjoyed getting wringing wet with sweat when I exercise.

5. I have often felt a sense of tension and excitement when about to take exercise.

6. I have often responded positively to an unexpected invitation to exercise despite having just finished my regular exercise.

7. I have felt that I become a real person only when I am exercising.

8. I have tended to use exercise as both a comfort and strength even when I have been perfectly fit and do not need any more.

9. I have often taken exercise just to tire myself sufficiently for sleep.

10. When I have gone out I have often taken sports clothes and equipment with me "just in case" the opportunity arises to exercise.

Shopping/Spending

1. I have felt uncomfortable when shopping with other people because it has restricted my freedom.

2. I have particularly enjoyed buying bargains so that I have often finished up with more than I need.

3. I have tended to use shopping and spending as both a comfort and strength even when I do not need anything.

4. I have tended to go shopping just in case I might see something I want.

5. When I have been shopping with family members, friends or other people, I have tended to disguise the full extent of my purchases.

6. I have often bought so many goods (groceries, sweets, household goods, books etc.) that it would take a month to get through them.

7. I have preferred to keep my shopping supplies topped up in case of war or natural disaster, rather than let my stocks run low.

8. I have bought things not so much as a means of providing necessities but more as a reward that I deserve for the stress that I endure.

9. I have felt that I become a real person only when shopping or spending.

10. I have often gone shopping to calm my nerves.

Continuing assessment of the significance of the total point count of the answers given in each of these questionnaires led us to believe that it might be appropriate to compare these numbers with those of the non-addictive population, with those who are addictive in some way but who do not have an eating disorder, and with those who do have an eating disorder. Although I still use the figure of a total of twenty points as the rule of thumb indicator of clinical significance, we created the following table to give a more specific range of cut-off points, first for men (in bold print) and then for women according to the percentage of other men or women who do *not* have that level of problem. For example, men scoring between ten and twenty points, or women scoring between twenty-five and twenty-nine points, on the food bingeing questionnaire will be in the seventieth percentile i.e. only thirty per cent of men or women in the general population score at that level.

	Low	Average	High	Cause for concern	Significant problem	Serious problem	Extreme problem
Percentile	10-40	50-60	70	80	90-95	97.5	99
FoodBingeing	**0 - 5**	**6 - 9**	**10 - 14**	**15 - 20**	**21 - 28**	**29 - 33**	**34 - 50**
Points	0 - 10	11 - 18	19 - 24	25 - 29	30 - 38	39 - 43	44 - 50
FoodStarving	**0 - 3**	**4 - 5**	**6 - 8**	**9 - 11**	**12 - 23**	**24 - 30**	**31 - 50**
Points	0 - 5	6 - 10	11 - 4	15 - 22	23 - 40	41 – 44	45 - 50
Work	**0 - 13**	**14 - 18**	**19 - 22**	**23 - 26**	**27 - 34**	**35 - 37**	**38 - 50**
Points	0 - 12	13 - 19	20 - 22	23 - 27	28 - 33	34 – 39	40 - 50
Exercise	**0 - 7**	**8 - 12**	**13 - 17**	**18 - 21**	**22 - 30**	**31**	**32 - 50**
Points	0 - 6	7 - 11	12 – 15	16 - 24	25 - 33	34 – 38	39 - 50
Shopping Spending	**0 - 4**	**5 - 8**	**9 - 13**	**14 - 19**	**20 - 25**	**26 - 32**	**33 - 50**
Points	0 - 12	13 - 18	19 - 22	23 - 28	29 - 36	37 – 40	41 - 50

My reason for generally sticking to a cut-off level of twenty points for significant problems is my clinical observation that there are differences between men and women in the addictive outlets that they choose. There may be the same proportion of men and women who are addicts - probably ten per cent or so - but disproportionately more women than men have eating disorders. Therefore a man who has some anorexic behaviour may be relatively rare among men but still not have a significant eating disorder. Further, the distinctions are not as absolute as the table might indicate. There is no absolute distinction between people who binge and those who starve. Often the same people will binge or starve at different times. People suffering from bulimia, who binge and then vomit or purge, and others whose crash diets end in binges, often score highly in both the bingeing and starving questionnaires. Also, when patients binge on food they commonly also binge on shopping and spending. When they starve they also tend to exercise excessively. Both bingers and starvers may bury themselves in work. There is a great deal of overlap so that individual variables get lost from view in a chart of overall averages.

Furthermore, what really matters is not so much the comparison with other men or women but specifically whether one has an addictive tendency. Correspondingly, anaemia is always individually important even though it is generally more common in some countries than in others. Men who suffer from the "nurturant of self" group of addictive outlets illustrated here, most commonly channel their addictive urges into work and exercise whereas women overeat or starve or become bulimic and will also tend to shop and spend compulsively. Incidentally, when women shop compulsively, they tend to buy food or clothes whereas men tend to buy books, computers, sports or gardening equipment or something to do with motor vehicles; but these sexual stereotypes are not always true. We do see men who binge or starve or shop compulsively and we frequently see anorexic women who exercise excessively and overeaters who take no exercise at all. Their average state is meaningless.

Consequently, I am not really interested in how one woman overeater compares with women in general or with men because there may be more women bingers in general than men and more women bingers and starvers than men. Nor am I particularly interested in comparing the numbers of male and female workaholics even though the proportion in each sex may be the same. My interest is primarily in identifying them. I think it better to keep things simple and look for the addictive characteristics upon which the questions were based rather than complicating matters in a maze of numbers. Thus a man scoring eleven points on the food starving questionnaire may be comparable to only twenty per cent of men but still not concern me from an addictive perspective because anorexia in men is rare and this skews the cut-off point downwards inappropriately if one is examining the general population.

Correspondingly, an overeating woman would definitely concern me on a score of twenty-two points even though thirty per cent of other women are like her. Not only are eating disorders common in women but there tend to be more overeating problems in women than in men because in our culture women tend to be more involved in food preparation. This does not mean that compulsive overeating is environmentally acquired rather than genetically linked. It means that those women who have the "nurturant of self" addictive tendency (which I believe is probably genetically inherited) will be more likely to express it in bingeing rather than, say, in work. Overeating women will therefore tend to skew the cut-off point upwards, just as in England the fact that ten per cent of the adult population drink fifty per cent of the total volume of alcohol consumed skews the average per capita consumption upwards.

The decision on which form of treatment is required (simple abstinence on its own or coupled with outpatient or inpatient professional care) will depend upon assessment of *the whole range* of addictive outlets rather than solely upon the answers to the bingeing questionnaire. That surely is what should really matter to me or to the patients.

The purpose of making this broad assessment of addictive behaviour is to show patients themselves the range and intensity of their addictive outlets. Patients commonly say "everyone I know does that", and it is helpful to show them that, while this may possibly be true, it indicates that they may have been selective in their friendships in choosing people who share their addictive behaviour.

It is important to treat patients in groups so that they can understand, support and challenge each other. One-to-one therapy is mostly what patients want but it does nothing to counter the psychopathology of denial, in which patients do not believe that they really have this specific problem. They need to be able to see other sufferers so that they can get the essential insight that their own problem is part of their genetic make-up rather than anything to do with the specific events of their childhood or current circumstances.

Some patients who have eating disorders will also have other addictive tendencies beyond the common cross-addictions of work; exercise, shopping and spending that form the "nurturant of self" group. They may also have some characteristics of the "hedonistic" group (alcohol, recreational drugs, prescription drugs, nicotine, caffeine, gambling and risk-taking, sex and love addiction). Other patients may have significant scores on the compulsive helping and relationship addiction questionnaires. Some may have widespread addictive behaviour across all three groups. In our experience of treating over three thousand inpatients over the last seventeen years, we find that the broader the range of addictive tendencies and the higher the scores within each individual addictive outlet, the higher the frequency of relapse.

This is not surprising but it emphasises the need to look at *all* addictive tendencies right at the start if one is to give these patients the best opportunity of recovery when they first enter treatment. What does interest me is the relative intensity of one addictive outlet compared with others. If all have the same cut-off point of twenty points for clinical significance, it enables patients to see immediately that they are at risk of relapse unless they look at *all* their significant addictive outlets. Leaving an addictive tendency unattended means that the underlying neurotransmission disease is being ineffectively addressed and will be perpetuated in one form or another, if not through its original addictive outlet. Patients who suffer recurrent relapses inevitably become dispirited - as will their counsellors - and they deserve better than that. Ignoring nicotine addiction - on the grounds that it can be dealt with later - or stimulating a prescription drug addiction by prescribing anti-depressants, on the grounds that these drugs help patients to be more functional, is fundamentally misconceived.

The idea that patients should not tackle everything at once dies hard but I believe that cross-addictions are the prime cause of relapse. This is obviously true if one believes that the problem goes primarily with the person rather than with one or another substance. Naturally, addicts of one kind or another will defend their alternative addictive outlets to the hilt - because without them they have to face up to their disturbed thoughts, feelings and behaviour without any of these emotional props. However, they have to live in the real world rather than escape from it. Naturally counsellors who are themselves still smoking cigarettes, or indulging in other addictive behaviour, would hotly disagree with this clinical approach - but they would, wouldn't they?

Ultimately the nature of recovery depends on what one considers to be true "recovery". This is a very different concept from mere abstinence from a particular addictive substance or behaviour. My own belief is that recovery should comprise:

i.   Peace of mind in spite of unsolved problems.

ii.   Happy, mutually fulfilling relationships.

iii. Spontaneity, creativity and enthusiasm.

These three characteristics of true recovery give life its colour and meaning. Anything less is, to my mind, less than patients deserve from us as their professional advisers. They deserve to have their neurotransmission disease fully addressed by people who understand it fully rather than have it treated half-heartedly.

Alcoholics Anonymous advises "we should be fearless and thorough from the very start". I totally support that principle with regard to all the addictive outlets of any individual patient and would agree that the best time to deal with them is right at the very start. As Alcoholics Anonymous points out, when patients say "What an order! I could not go through with that", we should reply, "Do not be discouraged. No one among us has been able to maintain anything like perfect adherence to these principles". However, this particular quotation refers to working the Twelve Step programme rather than only to being abstinent. As far as addictive substances are concerned, it is perfectly possible to be totally abstinent. Where the addictive behaviours are concerned, one can be abstinent from using that particular behaviour in an addictive way. For example, we all have to work and take exercise and shop and spend, but we do not have to do any of these things addictively (along the lines of the twelve addictive characteristics outlined earlier). Addicts of one kind or another know perfectly well when they are using an addictive process for its mood-altering effect rather than primarily for the purpose that any non-addict would use it. When an addict works or exercises, shops or spends addictively, it is primarily for the mood-altering effect rather than for what one might achieve as a member of the normal population. "Perfect adherence" may indeed not be possible in this respect - but one can give it an extremely good try, particularly if one does it alongside other people who are working the same programme of recovery.

When running a treatment centre, such as PROMIS, one has to temper the ideal with the practical. I once made the decision that the PROMIS Recovery Centre should be completely non-smoking. Immediately I lost four patients and two members of the counselling staff. Furthermore, I got a reputation "on the street" for being extreme - rather than for trying to be helpful - and this affected our recruitment of further patients. Faced with the prospect of going out of business altogether, I had to backtrack and say that we would help and encourage patients to give up smoking but would not insist upon it. I let the staff go.

I am uncomfortable with this policy of appeasement but I would be even more uncomfortable if the entire treatment centre were to close if I did not make this compromise. As far as counselling staff are concerned, we no longer recruit cigarette smokers because we believe that they would be incapable of advising patients on the treatment of one addictive disorder while themselves indulging in another. As far as PROMIS is concerned, we consider cigarette smokers to be active addicts if they score more than twenty points on the nicotine addiction assessment in the Shorter PROMIS Questionnaire. Nicotine, the addictive substance that they use, may be legal, despite the fact that it is the most damaging of all addictive substances (in the UK, all the recreational drugs put together kill fifteen people a day, alcohol kills one hundred people a day and nicotine kills three hundred people a day), but it is certainly addictive and therefore it should not be used at all by people who work in helping other people to understand and give up addictive behaviour. In diagnosing other people, it does us no harm whatever if we first attack this problem in ourselves.

Chapter Five
Abstinence

Bill W., one of the co-founders of Alcoholics Anonymous, wrote the *Big Book* of Alcoholics Anonymous and also the companion volume, *Twelve Steps and Twelve Traditions*. He also published a whole series of articles under the title, *As Bill Sees It*.

Dr Bob, the other co-founder, is remembered for just one saying: "Let's not louse the whole thing up. Let's keep it simple."

There are those who believe that Dr Bob's one statement was the most profound of all. Addicts tend to be compulsive complicators. Never is this truer than in the guidelines that tend to be written for sufferers from eating disorders.

In the PROMIS Recovery Centre in the last seventeen years we have treated over a thousand inpatients suffering from eating disorders. We should by now know something about the subject but it is remarkable how many people, sometimes with no clinical experience whatever, have absolute firm convictions on precisely what should or should not be done for patients with eating disorders.

The most vociferous of these are, of course, the potential new patients. The failure of their own ideas may be manifestly obvious in their compulsive behaviour but still they cling desperately to the very ideas that have resulted in so much destruction. Frequently patients from the anorexic end of the eating disorder spectrum will arrive at PROMIS with a long list of food substances that they simply cannot eat, often because "they cause allergic reactions". Correspondingly, patients from the compulsive overeating end of the eating disorder spectrum or those who are bulimic will arrive with a long list of substances that are "binge foods". Each is terrified of the food itself as if it had some magical property of its own. In the case of sugar and white (refined) flour, this is true: they have similar stimulant effects to those of cocaine for recreational drug addicts. They set up a craving for more.

At PROMIS we believe that these are virtually the only food substances that should be of concern to patients with eating disorders. It is the craving for more that causes the damage and therefore sufferers from eating disorders should focus primarily upon giving up those substances that cause cravings. There are people who binge on fats or fruit or almost anything but the subject of "binge foods" is really a different issue. Eating disorder sufferers will binge, once the initial craving has been stimulated, on whatever food substance they choose. This choice is a habit that can be broken, whereas the craving that is stimulated by sugar and white flour is a compulsion. It is sometimes thought to be paradoxical that at PROMIS we take anorexic patients off sugar and white flour, which are potentially fattening. Our hope in doing so is to demonstrate to the patient that it is only these substances that set up the frightening craving to eat more and more. If they avoid them they will not get the cravings and will hopefully begin to see that other foods can be eaten perfectly safely without that risk.

Similarly we tend to challenge patients on their concepts of food allergies, mineral and trace element deficiencies and intestinal candidiasis. These clinical conditions may exist, just as post-viral fatigue syndrome (M.E.) may exist, but there are times when individual patients are utterly convinced that they have one - or even all - of these problems when there is no evidence for that. Fortunately there are specific tests that can be done, such as blood tests to assess the total level of immunoglobulins and the specific responses to individual food substances and other potential allergens, gut fermentation tests to assess the possibility of intestinal candidiasis, and blood tests assessing the level of reaction to the Epstein Barr virus and also other viral tests when assessing post-viral fatigue syndrome (Myalgic Encephalopathy: M.E.). These three clinical conditions - food allergies, intestinal candidiasis and M.E. - are what I term "band-wagon" illnesses: they may genuinely affect some people but a lot of other patients may jump on the band-wagon in trying to make out that they themselves are special and different from the general population in these particular clinical respects. Their beliefs tend not to be substantiated by the proper clinical tests. The validity of these tests may be questioned but at least they provide some measure of scientific objectivity to counter the almost religious fervour with which patients may cling to these diagnoses.

Our experience at PROMIS is that patients may come in to treatment with all sorts of reasons why they cannot eat this or that but, by the time they leave treatment, they have switched their focus of attention to themselves rather than what is on the plate.

Some foods, such as salt and spices, are stimulants of the appetite. They can be used safely in cooking for patients with eating disorders but, as a general principle, they should not be added to food afterwards. Patients at the anorexic end of the eating disorder spectrum will at times try to flood their taste buds with salt or spices so that they get stimulus overload and hence turn on the satiety centre in the brain and switch off the appetite centre.

Once stimulated, the appetite centre in the brain tends to stay active for about twenty minutes. It is for this reason that patients of PROMIS are advised not to have any snacks between meals. If they feel hungry they should have a drink of water or milk or freshly squeezed fruit juice (other fruit juices often have a significant sugar content as preservatives even though the labels on the packets may describe them as being "sugar free"). For the same reason we advise patients who come from the compulsive overeating or bulimic end of the eating disorder spectrum to eat slowly so that a meal lasts at least twenty minutes. Otherwise they may bolt down a large quantity of food but still feel hungry. The exercise that we sometimes do on "gentle" eating, in which patients chew each mouthful to liquid before swallowing, demonstrates that the appetite centre reacts to time rather than quantity of food. Patients doing this exercise find that they are no longer hungry after twenty minutes even though they may have consumed much less than they would normally eat.

Canapés and other "cocktail" foods served before the main meal can be a disaster area for patients with eating disorders since they may stimulate a binge because of their high salt content. They also tend to prolong the meal beyond the twenty minutes of activity of the appetite centre so that, by the time they get to the meal itself, eating disorder patients are no longer eating to satisfy hunger, which is precisely what they need to learn to do. A meal that drags on and on - particularly a buffet or a meal taken in the homes of alcoholics who are inevitably more interested in the drink than in the food - can be very challenging for sufferers from eating disorders.

Alcohol is itself a refined carbohydrate and therefore should be avoided by sufferers from eating disorders. They may not have a risk of drinking progressively more alcohol, as would happen in an alcoholic, but there will be a risk of stimulating the desire to binge on food. The converse - suggesting to alcoholics that they should give up sugar and white flour - would not apply unless they coincidentally also have an eating disorder. People with any form of neurotransmission disease need to give up only those substances and processes that come within the particular group (hedonistic, nurturant of self, or compulsive helping and relationship addiction) from which they themselves suffer. On this basis sufferers from eating disorders might be able to use recreational drugs safely but we would not recommend that they should try to do so. Nicotine and caffeine are both frequently used as appetite suppressants by sufferers from eating disorders and are therefore probably dangerous for them. Compulsive helpers and relationship addicts, who have no other addictive tendency whatever, might be able to get away with using all sorts of addictive substances and processes, just as people who have no addictive tendency whatever can drink alcohol perfectly safely and may well be able to use other addictive substances and processes without the same risks as are run by people who have neurotransmission disease. These people may get damaged from being stupid - such as when driving while drunk - but they will be less inclined to do it again and again, as would be the case with people who have an addictive nature because of their neurotransmission disease. The problem is that people who do have neurotransmission disease are commonly determined to demonstrate that they have not got it. They can cause themselves great damage in the years during which they try to avoid facing up to their personal reality in this respect.

Conversely, people who do not have neurotransmission disease may be able to use mood-altering substances sensibly but it is bizarre that they should ever want to do so. There is no law that says one *has* to drink or smoke in order to be happy. There is certainly no law that says that recreational drugs are an essential part of a stimulating life. For addicts to use these substances, in order to keep themselves alive rather than submit to their suicidal depression, is one thing but for the normal population to use them when they have no inner psychological craving to do so is crazy and it provides sad evidence of the poverty of a human spirit that knows no better stimulus. To believe that happiness comes from a bottle or tablet or other substance is spiritual poverty indeed. In this respect sufferers from eating disorders can be just as stupid as anyone else and they need to examine the whole range of their behaviour, whether it be addictive or otherwise. There is no point in doing all the work that is necessary to get into recovery from an eating disorder only to spoil the end result by allowing oneself to be sucked into the mad behaviour of a philosophically inadequate society.

On exactly this same basis, there is no indication whatever for sufferers from eating disorders to be prescribed anti-depressants or other mood-altering prescription medications. Of course Prozac and other selective serotonin re-uptake inhibitors (the wonder drugs of the moment) "work" for bulimia, for which they are commonly prescribed, but so would heroin. On the same basis, heroin would work for toothache, in so far as it took away the pain, but it would do nothing for the underlying disorder of the tooth. Anti-depressants and other mood-altering prescription drugs therefore have nothing whatever to offer in the treatment of patients with eating disorders. They should be totally avoided. Patients need to be helped towards feeling the full range of their emotions and learning to react appropriately so that they have a full and stimulating life. The alternative of suppressing their feelings with sugar and white flour or with the mood-altering effects of bingeing, starving, vomiting or purging, leads to a drab and colourless existence. Great claims are often made for what is achieved through taking anti-depressants. The real tragedy of their widespread use is in observing what is taken away: the spontaneity, creativity and enthusiasm that are the essence of life itself.

The one pharmaceutical drug for which there might be a proper place in the treatment of eating disorders is Naltrexone. This is an anti-euphoriant, commonly used in the treatment of recreational drug addicts in order to take away any "buzz" that they might get from taking heroin. The drug is used as an aid to prevent relapse. The idea is that Naltrexone blocks the opiate receptors in the brain and patients will not take heroin if they find that it achieves nothing in the way of mood alteration. On the same principle Naltrexone is sometimes used to help patients suffering from alcoholism maintain their abstinence. At PROMIS we do not use Naltrexone either for recreational drug addicts or for alcoholics because we believe that the best way of maintaining recovery comes through attendance at regular meetings of the Anonymous Fellowships and through working the Twelve Step programme. This mood-altering process is quite sufficient on a continuing basis to counter the suicidal depression of neurotransmission disease. Anything else is superfluous. The use of pharmaceutical substances is dangerous for any patients suffering from any form of addictive behaviour. They may come to believe that the solution to all their problems can, after all, be found in a bottle or a tablet.

For this reason at PROMIS we use pharmaceutical drugs only for a short period of detoxification at the beginning of treatment. It is precisely for this process that I believe one should use Naltrexone, one tablet daily for the first month of treatment, in patients suffering from anorexia. It takes away the mood-altering effects - in particular the sense of total control - of starvation. The great challenge in anorexia is in the double negative: how does one help someone *not* to *not* do something? By taking Naltrexone for the first month of treatment, the anorexic patients lose that sense of total control through starvation because it no longer produces a mood-altering effect. Even so, these patients should not be prescribed Naltrexone for longer than one month because otherwise they would risk becoming dependent upon using a substance. This psychological - even if not physiological – dependency upon

Naltrexone would prevent them from developing the alternative mood alteration of reaching out to help someone else anonymously within the Twelve Step Fellowships.

It is this alternative mood-altering process of working the Twelve Step programme that is ultimately the source of daily remission from any form of addictive behaviour. The neurotransmission disease persists but it receives daily appropriate treatment that is life enhancing. As a result of working the Twelve Step programme, sufferers from neurotransmission disease are able to enjoy the full range of colour in their emotional lives. This is exactly what is lost in the addictive use of mood-altering substances and processes. In particular it is lost when patients are prescribed anti-depressants or other mood-altering prescription medications.

One would have hoped that Aldous Huxley's warning in *Brave New World* would have taught us the dangers of prescription medications - but to judge from the frequency of their current use - apparently not. Perhaps some doctors (through the peculiarities of their training in "scientific" medicine with a dominant focus upon pharmacology and therapeutics) have become so engrossed in "treatment" that they have totally lost sight of philosophical values.

Chapter Six
Childhood Trauma

We all of us suffer childhood trauma to some degree. No one has a perfect childhood. In any case, if someone were to do so, it would not be a very satisfactory training for adult life. We have to learn to work our way through our disappointments, surmount challenges and get over the various hurts and deprivations that we may suffer. This is not to advocate that we should all wear hair shirts, nor to diminish the significance of the very real traumas that some children endure. However, it does emphasise that all life is a challenge. There is never a time when we can sit back and relax, secure in the knowledge that all our difficulties are in the past. Rather, we should get into the habit of recognising that difficult challenges are in fact opportunities for further understanding and growth. Not only should we learn from our own experience but hopefully we can learn to be more understanding and considerate towards others so that we do not perpetuate the emotional abuse and abandonment that we ourselves may have endured.

There are people who believe that eating disorders and other outlets for neurotransmission disease are primarily caused by childhood trauma. There is no evidence to support this. For example, whilst it is true that many bulimic patients have been sexually abused in childhood, it is not true that children who have been sexually abused necessarily grow up to become bulimic. The sad fact is that sexual abuse is common and only a few of the children who have been sexually abused grow up to have problems with addictive behaviour of one kind or another.

The confusion arises because, just as neurotransmission disease - with all its attendant addictive behaviours - runs in families, so does abuse and abandonment. This does not mean that abuse and abandonment are genetically inherited traits. It means that people in the active phase of their addiction tend to be totally self-centred and abusive of others. Thus, someone who is alcoholic or otherwise addicted may abuse or abandon all his or her children equally, but only some of these children - those who inherited the genetic predisposition to neurotransmission disease - will themselves develop it in one outlet or another or, more commonly, in several at the same time. Thus, those patients who believe that their addictive behaviour was *caused* by abuse and abandonment in childhood should examine their own siblings - or children from other families who have been abused or abandoned - to see that very often they develop no addiction problems at all. To be sure, there is a great deal of damage done by childhood abuse and abandonment but that is a separate problem, totally distinct from whether or not one develops an addictive tendency.

I believe that the development of any specific addictive outlet is a three-stage process:

i   The antecedent cause: the genetically inherited defect in neurotransmission in the mood centres of the brain.

ii.   The contributory cause: some form of traumatic episode that awakens the need for mood-alteration.

iii. The precipitant cause: the exposure to a mood-altering substance or process that works for that individual.

If we lack any one of these three factors we will not develop that specific addictive outlet. For example:

If we do not have the genetic predisposition, then we will not become addicts of any kind. The Vietnam war veterans' study showed that most GIs who used addictive drugs during their tours of combat duty were able to get off them after returning home and were able to use alcohol, and perhaps other mood-altering substances, without progressive harm. They may have been physiologically addicted - developing withdrawal symptoms when the addictive substances were not available - but they were not spiritually addicted: they had no inner craving, driving them towards further use of mood-altering substances or processes. Ten per cent of the drug-using GIs, however, were not able to stay away from further addictive behaviour and were not able to use mood-altering substances such as alcohol sensibly. One has only to remember the young man playing Russian roulette in that beautiful film, *The Deer Hunter*, or the sea captain who lost both his legs in that other beautiful film, *Forrest Gump*, to see examples of combat veterans who were still trapped in the throes of active addiction.

The findings of the Vietnam War veterans' study are hotly disputed between the two opposing camps of psychological treatment:

a. Psychiatrists and others who believe that the study demonstrates that everybody *could* get off drugs but only some weak-willed or otherwise inadequate souls did not do so.

b. Those who believe that the study demonstrates that ten per cent of the population have a genetically inherited defect in neurotransmission whereas the rest do not.

It would be absolutely extraordinary if such a delicate and complex organ as the human brain did not provide examples of genetically inherited defects. After all, the liver, the kidneys, the adrenal glands, the thyroid glands, the pancreas and everything else in the body have genetically inherited defects, giving rise to particular clinical syndromes. The brain surely cannot have escaped this risk. We are aware of genetically inherited conditions - such as Down's syndrome - in which the mental facilities are impaired. It would be incredible if the mood centres of the brain were not to have corresponding examples of defective function.

Just because a particular condition is genetically inherited does not mean that it will necessarily be transmitted to all offspring. Other genes may have been inherited from the other parent or a particular condition may require a particular set of interactions between a number of genes, not all of which may have been inherited by a particular child.

The importance of considering whether a particular characteristic is inherited or acquired is that it will determine the appropriate treatment. For a genetically inherited condition one has no choice but to accept it and, if possible, learn to avoid its potential influence on a day-to-day basis. For example, until the days of corneal surgery, there was nothing one could do about short sight other than wear spectacles or contact lenses on a day-to-day basis. Neither of these procedures changed the short sight but they enabled the individual to function more or less normally. There were still some things that he or she could not do - such as see under water or fly a fighter aircraft - but otherwise there were very few limitations on what he or she could do alongside other people. Equally there was nothing magnificent or virtuous in wearing spectacles or contact lenses. Nor did spectacles or contact lenses provide an unfair advantage over other people or mean that books could be read or cars driven by magic: the same lessons had to be learned and the same work had to be done as for anyone else. This is a good parallel to the Twelve Step programme treatment for neurotransmission disease and its various addictive outlets. The underlying condition - the neurotransmission disease - is still there but specific addictive outlets can be countered on a day-to-day basis through abstinence and through working the Twelve Step programme. This simply puts the sufferer level with other people, but lessons have to be learned and work done just the same: there is no magical formula that provides something for nothing simply because one works a Twelve Step programme.

Where difficulties are acquired, rather than genetically inherited, there is a great deal that can be done that is curative. Analytical psychotherapeutic approaches and cognitive behavioural therapy will help with understanding the origin of various disorders of interpretation and hence of behaviour. Choice Theory, Rational Emotive Behaviour Therapy, Gestalt Therapy, Transactional Analysis, Rogerian Person-Centred Counselling and Neurolinguistic Programming can all help towards changing insight and hence behaviour. However, these are all "left brain", intellectual functions and they may be ineffective in trying to treat "right brain" emotional trauma that has resulted in post-traumatic stress disorder. These will require either psychodrama or EMDR (Eye Movement Desensitisation and Reprocessing) in order that effects of emotional trauma can become accessible to rational intervention.

Sufferers from eating disorders who have had serious abuse or abandonment in childhood may well have "right brain" imprints of post-traumatic stress disorder. These will be a contributory cause of continuing problems with eating disorders and other addictive or compulsive tendencies even though they were not the antecedent, genetic, cause.

The emotional effects may be deep-seated and persistent despite all manner of "talking" therapy. However, they can be resolved through psychodrama or EMDR and the long-term traumatic effects can be totally resolved. The genetically inherited addictive tendency will none the less remain.

Thus sufferers from eating disorders and other addictive or compulsive tendencies who have also suffered serious abuse or abandonment in childhood will need to have a two-pronged approach. The first is to counter the genetically inherited neurotransmission disease through abstinence and through working the Twelve Step programme of the Anonymous Fellowships. The second is to counter the post-traumatic stress disorder, caused by abuse and abandonment, through psychodrama and EMDR.

In addition, a whole range of other therapeutic approaches, such as those mentioned previously, could be helpful for that part of his or her emotional life, which the eating disorder sufferer has in common with the normal population. These therapeutic approaches – regardless of their claims - have nothing whatever to offer in the treatment of addictive or compulsive behaviour as such, but they have a great deal to offer in the treatment of the various complexes, confusions and crises that befall us all and which may affect sufferers from neurotransmission disease as much as anyone else. This is comparable to the treatment offered to patients who may have two co-existing physical conditions: someone with diabetes needs the specific treatment for that condition but will also need surgical treatment for an acute appendicitis if that occurs: having the treatment for diabetes is no protection against getting appendicitis. Correspondingly, people who suffer from neurotransmission disease cannot afford to forget that they are part of the human race and therefore just as likely as anyone else, if not more so, to suffer the slings and arrows of outrageous fortune or get any other problem that can affect anyone else.

When it comes to treating the effects of emotional trauma in the childhood and earlier life of patients suffering from eating disorders or other outlets of neurotransmission disease, the starting position has to be to get rid of the self-pity and blame that tend to characterise addictive or compulsive behaviour. These patients need to be helped to acknowledge that the abuse or abandonment really did occur - it is not healthy for it to be denied - and also to accept that it was wrong, indeed totally unacceptable. Only then can they be helped to move on - which they have to do if they are to have healthy emotional lives in future. To continue to wallow in self-pity and blame is unhealthy in the extreme, and this is not helped by attendance at meetings of Co-dependents Anonymous or meetings of Adult Children of Alcoholics. These particular Anonymous Fellowships tend to perpetuate the problem by implying that abuse and abandonment have resulted in a permanent negative imprint that is untreatable.

The other disadvantage of these two Anonymous Fellowships is that they focus primarily upon someone else's behaviour - that of a parent or other care-giver in early childhood - rather than following the example of other Anonymous Fellowships that focus the attention exclusively on the sufferer's own behaviour. Ultimately we cannot change other people's behaviour; we can change only our own. We have to learn to become responsible not only for our actions but also for our reactions. Similarly, we learn to accept responsibility for our feelings when we recognise that they come as a direct result of our behaviour being in harmony or at discord with our values. No one else has the power to *make* us feel happy or sad: we respond to their statements or actions in accordance with the principles of our own personal philosophy over which we alone have total control.

Patients who want to believe that their disturbed feelings and behaviour are all the responsibility of other people or events or circumstances have a long, hard road to climb. Eventually they have to come to accept, like the rest of us, that life may be difficult but it is up to each one of us to live our own lives to the best of our ability. Our self-esteem is not something that can be given to us or taken away by other people. It is ultimately entirely a product of our own determination to establish our own values and live our lives according to those principles. Whatever anyone else may or may not have done to us in our past lives, or do at present, is irrelevant. This may seem hard but, as M Scott Peck said in the opening words of *The Road Less Travelled* (Arrow, 1999), "Life is difficult".

Chapter Seven
Having a Chronic Illness

Nobody votes in favour of having a chronic (long-term) illness. We would all much rather have something that was temporary and preferably treatable with surgery. "Cut it out, throw the bad bit away and sew up the wound" is the ideal therapeutic principle. "Take a tablet for a time to make it better or help you sort it out" would be the next to ideal treatment. "Learn how to live with this condition and diminish its effects on a day-to-day basis" does not have quite the same ring as the other two.

In general patients do not like the idea of having to live with a condition and they are reluctant to take on the discipline of daily adjustments to behaviour. However, patients with neurotransmission disease, or any other chronic disease, have to do exactly this.

Sufferers from chronic illnesses of any kind fight against this acceptance every inch of the way. They would rather have almost any other diagnosis. They don't mind accepting that they have been traumatised and they are usually content to be given a diagnosis of depression, particularly if they can attribute it to the words or actions of someone else, and they will even accept that they have had some form of "breakdown" because that concept relieves them of personal responsibility. However, a diagnosis of a chronic illness due to an addictive or compulsive nature will be totally and absolutely rejected, not only by the sufferer, but often also by friends and family and by colleagues at work, if they get to hear of it. That diagnosis seems preposterous and even offensive.

Accepting the diagnosis of a chronic illness requires a process of surrender and this goes against the grain of our upbringing and culture: we are taught to fight, not to give in. However, there is a fundamental difference between fighting against difficult odds and fighting against impossible odds and these should not be confused. It shows even greater courage to surrender, recognising that one is totally defeated, than it does to continue fighting when there is not only a possibility but even a probability that things will not work out well. We admire Butch Cassidy and the Sundance Kid when they come out for their final battle, knowing that they are in deep trouble. We may not admire what they did that brought them to that dreadful final day of reckoning but we admire their spirit in fighting on. The fact that they were annihilated leaves us sad, but we still admire the magnificence of their failure.

For people who are fighting against neurotransmission disease there is a similarity to Butch Cassidy and the Sundance Kid in that they go on fighting to the very last. Many do indeed fight to the death and lose their lives in the battle against impossible odds. Fortunately, many nowadays have the opportunity to surrender and begin a new life, working the Twelve Step programme. This is a new daily battle requiring considerable courage at first. As time goes on, however, the daily battle is transformed into a daily reprieve: they come to recognise that life is easier when an addictive tendency is accepted rather than fought. Of course there are also battles to be fought professionally and personally, socially and culturally, but those are the same battles that anyone else has to fight. The battle against neurotransmission disease, however, comes to be seen as utterly pointless. There is no chance whatever of victory. There is only the absolute certainty of the grave. Therefore, it becomes increasingly obvious that surrender is a sensible as well as a brave choice in this particular battle.

Retrospectively, from a distance of some years after that final surrender, people who have fought and lost the battle against neurotransmission disease and finally accepted the need to surrender, come to see that it was the most sensible decision they ever took in their lives. What on earth had been the point of continuing to use addictive substances and processes that were so damaging? Why on earth did they ever believe that these substances and processes could have been so vital, so central to life itself? Why did they ever need to binge or starve, use alcohol or drugs? None of these things is of any fundamental importance to a happy life – but that recognition comes only retrospectively. At the time of surrender there is no such balanced perspective: addictive substances and processes really do seem at that time to be a central necessity of life. This is precisely why surrender is delayed for so long and why it is such a courageous act when its necessity is finally acknowledged.

Many people in the Anonymous Fellowships who work a Twelve Step programme, in relation to one addictive substance or another, may do so sincerely and determinedly yet still resist surrender to the battle against neurotransmission disease itself. They may be prepared to give up one substance but still be reluctant to acknowledge that they have to give up *all* the addictive substances and processes that affect them. They believe that they have done enough – or at least as much as could be reasonably expected of them – and they don't see why they should give up even more of their limited "pleasures". This "stinking thinking", as it is known in Alcoholics Anonymous, inevitably eventually leads back to relapse. Ultimately they need to examine whether it is worth having "pleasures" that can be so destructive. Is there really nothing else in life that can provide real pleasure without at the same time risking everything one holds dear?

We have a strange society in this respect: alcohol, nicotine, caffeine and sugar are often thought to be not only pleasurable but also necessary. Looked at dispassionately, this attitude is utterly bizarre. What about friendship? What about a love of literature and the arts? What about the innocence and beauty of spending time with children? All these things can be tragically put at risk when people think of mood-altering substances and processes as "pleasures" or "necessities". Ultimately there is a straight choice: to be chronically ill or chronically well. The rewards of working a Twelve Step programme are immense. Not only does one avoid the negative consequences of using mood-altering substances and processes, one gains a vast amount of time and opportunity for focused attention upon things that give real pleasure in life. In this respect, sufferers from neurotransmission disease are uniquely blessed in having a chronic illness from which full remission on a day-to-day basis is possible. The sufferers from rheumatoid arthritis, disseminated sclerosis, ankylosing spondylitis, motor neurone disease and even diabetes or psoriasis would be glad to know that they had the possibility of just one day of remission from their chronic illnesses.

But addicts of one kind or another tend to wallow in self-pity and in blaming other people. Far from seeing the glass as half full, they see it as half empty. They see the prospect of recovery in terms of something that they are going to lose rather than gain. Such self-obsession is highly unattractive. An attitude of gratitude, bringing hope and happiness to their own lives and to others each day would be more in order. Those of us who have suffered from neurotransmission disease are exceedingly fortunate to have a condition that is so readily treatable on a day-to-day basis and we should be grateful for that.

Chapter Eight
Treatment

The physical treatment of patients with eating disorders can at times be very demanding but nothing like so demanding as the psychological treatment. Helping people to put on weight or take it off is a relatively straightforward matter of controlling the food intake and exercise output. People who are undernourished can be helped to put on weight through having regularly supervised meals and high-calorie liquid supplements and they can even be fed through a naso-gastric tube or intravenous infusion if life is at risk.

People who are overweight can have "plated" meals, where the portion size is predetermined by someone else. People who are bulimic can be locked out of the lavatories and personally supervised for one hour after each meal.

All these approaches are possible - even though some of them may require intervention by the Courts - but they are pointless unless the psychological problem is dealt with at the same time.

In the circumstance of extreme anorexia, the psychological problem is inaccessible: the brain is so shrivelled, along with the body, that it shuts out any outside influence. It is in these extreme circumstances that recourse to the Mental Health Act may be indicated. As mentioned previously, prescribing one tablet of Naltrexone a day as an anti-euphoriant may also be a sensible starting point for the first month of treatment in order to help counter the absolute madness of anorexic self-destruction. Patients who are at the compulsive overeating or bulimic end of the eating disorder spectrum require no medication. All they need, alongside those at the anorexic end of the spectrum, is the support and challenge of a group of patients suffering from similar conditions.

At PROMIS we see all addictive behaviour as being essentially the same process, irrespective of which particular addictive outlet may be used in the self-administered "treatment" of the underlying neurotransmission disease. However, this view is often not shared by the families of patients with eating disorders. They may dislike the idea of their sons and daughters, husbands or wives, having anything whatever in common with alcoholics and drug addicts. They fear that they might learn new destructive habits from those patients. On this issue PROMIS has given up the unequal struggle and we have now built a separate treatment centre in London primarily for patients with eating disorders.

Doctors, counsellors and therapists often share those misgivings. Our own contrary experience is that patients learn much more about neurotransmission disease by seeing it in *all* its manifestations across the whole range of addictive behaviour. They see what they are really up against, rather than continuing to believe that the problem is more in the substance than in the person. There is in fact a risk that, in a specifically designated eating disorder unit, patients will learn "eating disorder tricks" from each other. This can be exactly what happens in units that focus only upon food and body weight - and throw in a bit of cognitive behavioural therapy - as opposed to Minnesota Method units that focus primarily upon the interdependence of patients to help them get better. Patients may want to be isolated in their rooms and to have one-to-one therapy in which they talk about all the difficulties of their childhoods and subsequent adult lives - but that is not what gets them better. They need the exposure, in group therapy sessions of one kind or another, morning, afternoon and evening, day after day, to the support and challenge of other patients who are similarly involved in tackling their distorted self-perceptions and learning a new set of principles, attitudes and behaviours one day at a time.

A major part of the early days or weeks in treatment will be spent in digging out false perceptions. One cannot teach people anything new if they believe that they already know all the answers. Often, at the time that patients come to PROMIS, they will have had many years of "treatments" of one kind or another that have mostly been instigated by themselves. In PROMIS they mostly learn from each other, through recognising that those methods of "treatment" that they have tried for themselves have not worked any better for the other patients.

Once they have recognised that, they will need to develop new perceptions on what does work - and what does not - in the treatment of eating disorders. They are helped considerably in this process by observing previous patients who are now doing very well. PROMIS invites previous patients to visit the Recovery Centre every Saturday evening for specific talks to the existing patients. We also have a system in which former patients in the first year of their recovery are invited back to spend one weekend at PROMIS every month. This has the dual benefit of exposing the new patients to people who have had successful treatment and it reminds the former patients of where they came from. Both benefit: the existing patients get encouragement and inspiration, the former patients get healthy reminders of the potential price of relapse.

An important part of the first two or three weeks of treatment at PROMIS is to wean patients gently off the anti-depressants that they may previously have been prescribed. Obviously they are weaned off appetite suppressants, including amphetamines, because these are addictive drugs in their own right. Exactly the same general principle applies to tranquillisers, anti-depressants and sleeping tablets: they are addictive to people who suffer from neurotransmission disease. In any case, they do not help patients to deal with the realities of their lives: they smother them. They also impede any development of true emotions. At PROMIS patients are encouraged to feel sad when unfortunate things happen, just as they are encouraged to feel happy when life has more fortunate turns. The problem with anti-depressants, tranquillisers and sleeping tablets is that they may superficially protect patients from bad feelings but they also remove the good ones. The end result is that patients lose the capacity to make appropriate judgements. This is a dreadful plight, to lose the capacity to distinguish between beauty and ugliness, happiness and sadness, freedom and imprisonment. All that remains is internal indifference, a life without colour or value.

Detoxification from sugar and white flour takes about ten days and patients have to be warned of the common withdrawal symptoms that they might experience: headaches, dizziness and irritability. Patients who have given up recreational drugs will sometimes tell us that they found withdrawal from sugar and white flour just as difficult. At the same time we recommend patients to give up caffeine. Withdrawal symptoms from caffeine also include headaches, dizziness and irritability. It is only when one gives up these substances that one realises just how addictive they are and how much one has become dependent upon them physiologically as well as emotionally. A life without them is not deprived: it is enhanced.

The basic work in a Minnesota Method treatment centre such as PROMIS is in helping patients to begin to develop an understanding of the Twelve Step programme of the Anonymous Fellowships. I have put the Steps mostly in the future tense in this example so as to emphasise that recovery comes as a result of *working* them in the Anonymous Fellowships rather than simply becoming familiar with them in a treatment centre.

Step I: I admit that I am powerless over the mood-altering substances, behaviours and relationships that affect me and that my life has become unmanageable.

Step II: I shall come to believe that a power greater than myself could restore me to sanity.

Step III: I shall make a decision to turn my will and my life over to the care of God *as I understand Him*.

Step IV: I shall make a searching and fearless moral inventory of myself.

Step V: I shall admit to God, to myself and to another human being the exact nature of my wrongs.

Step VI: I shall become entirely ready to have God remove all my defects of character.

Step VII: I shall humbly ask Him to remove my shortcomings.

Step VIII: I will make a list of all persons I have harmed and become willing to make amends to them all.

Step IX: I shall make direct amends to such people wherever possible, except when to do so would injure them or others

Step X: I shall continue to take a personal inventory and when I am wrong promptly admit it.

Step XI: I shall seek through prayer and meditation to improve my conscious contact with God _as I understand Him_, praying only for knowledge of His will for me and the power to carry that out.

Step XII: Having had a spiritual awakening as the result of these Steps, I shall try to carry this message to others who still suffer and to practise these principles in all my affairs.

Initially patients may see the word "God" and want to run a mile but the Twelve Steps themselves are quite specific in emphasising (in italics and underlined) "_as I understand Him_". (The Twelve Steps were written at a time when it was understood that 'Him' included 'Her' or even 'It').

At PROMIS we work through all these Twelve Steps in group therapy sessions - giving patients a basic understanding of the need to _work_ them and the benefits from doing so. Each patient – or student, as we call them – will come to work them in much greater depth after they have left treatment and when they are under the guidance of a "sponsor" (a fellow member of an Anonymous Fellowship who has had greater experience in working the Steps). The reason we encourage patients to work through the Twelve Steps in group therapy sessions - allowing patients to some extent to select the members of the group – is because of the old Alcoholics Anonymous saying that we are "as sick as our secrets". The more we hang on to guilt and shame, the more it poisons us. The more we bring it out into the open, the better our chance of making a new life and of making appropriate amends, wherever possible, to those we have harmed.

By the time patients leave PROMIS, they should be aware of the need for ongoing regular attendance at meetings of the Anonymous Fellowships and, in particular, the need for continuing work on the Twelve Steps on a daily basis. Indeed, the true recovery rate at PROMIS, as with all other treatment centres, is zero: recovery is obtainable _only_ through working the Twelve Steps in the Anonymous Fellowships. What PROMIS is able to do is to help a larger number of people to recover in the Anonymous Fellowships than would otherwise do so.

In the course of patients' treatment, our counselling staff will employ any number of therapeutic approaches, most particularly Choice Theory, Cognitive Behavioural Therapy, Gestalt, Transactional Analysis, Psychodrama and EMDR, depending upon the training, experience and personal enthusiasm of each individual counsellor. We generally avoid one-to-one therapy, although each patient or student has an individual Focal Counsellor to provide brief reminders, because vulnerable patients can only too easily form dependent relationships with individual counsellors. By the same token, counsellors may sometimes become too wrapped up in an individual patient's problems to be able to see clearly and dispassionately.

Ultimately, patients need to develop interdependent relationships with their peer group because this is what they are going to need to depend upon in the Anonymous Fellowships for the rest of their lives.

Counsellors, as with parents and family and friends, can love and provide an environment of love but cannot do someone else's loving - and it is this feature which is the essence of recovery. When A reaches out to help B anonymously, it is A who gets the benefit every time. B may or may not do so. By taking their minds off themselves and putting them on to other people, sufferers from eating disorders and other forms of addictive behaviour get rid of the self-centredness that has dogged them all their lives and learn to become focused upon the needs of other people. This is a lovely philosophy and it is quite extraordinary that it should at times be criticised so hotly by people who are not even familiar with it, let alone put it into practice in their own lives. Sometimes the Twelve Step programme may be seen as a threat to professional interests.

At PROMIS we are absolutely clear that the counselling staff do *not* get the patients better: patients learn how to get each other better. It takes considerable maturity for staff to be able to accept that they work hard every day - and deserve the credit for doing just that – but, even so, should not look to their patients for personal rather than professional gratitude.

Once sufferers from eating disorders graduate from PROMIS, they may go on to an extended care facility, a "Halfway House". In these houses patients share the accommodation with each other and may also go to regular outpatient therapeutic sessions but, at the same time, they are exposed to the real outside world in contrast with the sheltered environment of the inpatient treatment centres. The outside world has all the challenges that patients need to learn to deal with on a day-to-day basis - but they know that they can return to the relative shelter of the Halfway House when things are difficult. Ultimately, they have to break completely free and become dependent totally upon the inter-relationship with others in the Anonymous Fellowships. Here, particularly in the case of the eating disorder Fellowships, there can be some significant difficulties because the Fellowships themselves are not strong.

In Overeaters Anonymous there is no specific definition of abstinence other than "to abstain from compulsive overeating". How on earth would one know how to do that if one does *not* know how to do it? The history of Overeaters Anonymous was that the co-founders, who had a common background in Gamblers Anonymous, wrote down the list of all the foods that they themselves found challenging. The summary was put onto a grey sheet of paper and this list became the "Grey Sheet" recommendations for abstinence. It soon became apparent that this was unworkable: people became obsessed with physical abstinence just as they had previously been obsessed with bingeing. Bulimics Anonymous and Anorexics Anonymous have a similar reluctance to provide specific programmes of abstinence.

Over all, these Anonymous Fellowships leave sufferers from eating disorders to make their own decisions on physical abstinence. However, in practice those who have achieved long-term recovery from eating disorders tend to use the following guidelines:

i.   Abstinence from sugar and white flour and other refined carbohydrates, including alcohol.

ii. Three regular meals a day with nothing in between.

iii. Normal portion sizes, judged on what other people are taking.

iv. No added salt or spices.

At the same time they will need to be aware of other addictive substances and processes and, where specifically appropriate for themselves, cut them out. It should be emphasised that mere abstinence is not enough. Eating disorders do not respond simply to willpower or to dietary regimes. Sufferers have to attend regular meetings of Overeaters Anonymous or another appropriate Anonymous Fellowship and work the Twelve Step programme of recovery. They need to read the Fellowship literature on a regular basis and get a sponsor to guide them on their journey so that they no longer try to work everything out for themselves.

The programme is in fact very straightforward and simple - but addicts are compulsive complicators and will always try to find ways of ducking and diving, weaving and manipulating and generally trying to control rather than surrender. The guidance of other members of the Anonymous Fellowships is therefore vital to continuing recovery.

Even here, however, there can be traps. Somehow the notion of "food sponsors" has crept into the Anonymous Fellowships. Sufferers may be encouraged to telephone in to their "food sponsor" the food they intend to eat that day. In my view this is a totally obsessive and unnecessary and even destructive process. It continues to focus on the food rather than on the person.

An even greater obsession is found in those sufferers who still work a "Grey Sheet" programme of abstinence. Even worse is the "HOW" programme in which portion sizes are rigidly controlled, even by taking a small set of scales and a set of scissors to restaurants so that the exact quantity of meat or other foodstuffs can be weighed out before consumption. In my view this is absolutely crazy, with the sufferers continuing to be dominated by food and its hidden power. There is nothing hidden about the power of sugar and refined carbohydrates to lead to cravings; this is a common experience of people suffering from eating disorders. However, there is no such power in any other food substance. Binge foods such as fats or fruit - or anything that any particular sufferer may have used - can safely be reintroduced when recovery is sufficiently stable to take on the further challenge of new experience and trust.

Ultimately people recovering from eating disorders discover the fundamental truth that food was never the problem, other than in the capacity of sugar, white flour and other refined carbohydrates to cause cravings. The problem is an internal one; in the thoughts, feelings and behaviour of the individual sufferer - and those are what need to change.

Chapter Nine
Observing the Results

The proof of the validity of any idea has to be in whether or not it works in practice. The worlds of politics and religion are full to overflowing with ideas - but do they work in practice? The worlds of psychology and psychiatry are also full to overflowing with ideas. But do they work in practice?

The history of the ideas of the Twelve Step programme is fascinating and is outlined in *Not-God* by Ernest Kurtz (Hazelden, 1991). This book is well worth reading for its historical account but it occurs to me that one factor is supremely important: the ideas took root because they worked in practice. In the UK, even today, these ideas are largely ignored in university courses in psychology and psychiatry. The British National Health Service has no Minnesota Method treatment centres of any stature.

It is often suggested that patients should go to Alcoholics Anonymous when no other clinical approach has worked, but those who make this suggestion have very rarely attended an open meeting of Alcoholics Anonymous or even have any idea of the basics of the Twelve Step programme other than that it has something to do with God. This erroneous connection between a spiritual programme and religious belief is the cause not only of a great deal of confusion but of some hostile rejection. Yet, as emphasised in *Not- God*, the founders of Alcoholics Anonymous went to great pains to emphasise that theirs was *not* a religious programme even though the Twelve Steps were a development of the Five Steps of the Oxford Movement headed by Buchman. The spiritual concepts of the Anonymous Fellowships are not those of religion. They refer to the human spirit, the God within each one of us.

In the Big Book of Alcoholics Anonymous there is a whole chapter devoted to atheists and agnostics, showing how these rejections of standard theist belief should be no bar to attendance at meetings of Alcoholics Anonymous or to working the Twelve Step programme. The repeated emphasis on God *as you understand Him* could not be more clear in specifying that an orthodox religious belief is compatible with working a Twelve Step programme but it is not essential for it. I myself have no religious belief whatever yet I work a Twelve Step programme on a day-to-day basis in complete comfort alongside others who may have specific religious beliefs of one kind or another. My "God" is "other people". I learnt from years of isolation that I run my own life extremely badly when I do not take account of other people. I have learnt from personal experience the truth of John Donne's saying, "No man is an island". I learnt for myself my interdependence with other people. I learnt the hard way - ultimately in isolation in a side ward in a mental nursing home to which I had been admitted on diagnosis of "depression". Paradoxically I am grateful for that experience because it taught me that I cannot survive in isolation. I need other people to keep me sane.

That same discovery is the essential "entrance fee" paid by every new member of the Anonymous Fellowships. We learn that we are powerless over our addiction - of any kind - and that our lives have become unmanageable while we ourselves run them. This comprises the first Step. In the second Step we learn to believe that a higher power than self is what we need to help us move forward. Progressively we work through the other Steps, discovering that each in turn gives new opportunities for growth in our understanding and in the stability of our lives.

But all this individual experience would be nothing more than a passing curiosity if it were not supported by the experience of others. The fact that something works for me is of no great relevance - but the fact that it works for millions of people is highly relevant, particularly when they come from diverse backgrounds. However much universities and medical schools may try to ignore Twelve Step ideas, the observable fact is that they work in practice, as literally millions of people have discovered for themselves.

As far as recovery from eating disorders is concerned, the end results are observable in many people, despite the confusion over the definition of abstinence. In fact this confusion is in line with the basic Fellowship principle of not making rules for other people. We each have our own journey and we each make our own discoveries. Nonetheless it is helpful to see the effects of other people's journeys and it was this that persuaded me to establish the principles of abstinence adopted by PROMIS. I saw people who were doing well and people who were not doing so well and I looked to see what they had in common or what divided them. I would suggest that other people do exactly the same: don't take my word but look to see whether the quality of someone else's life is something that you yourself would want. If that person appears to be happy and to have good personal and professional relationships, is kind and considerate and free from food obsession, then it is worth following his or her ideas on abstinence. If, on the other hand, he or she is full of self-pity and blame, still talking about the abuse and abandonment of childhood and still obsessed in one way or another with food, then I, for one, would not wish to follow that person's ideas on abstinence. What matters to me is what works in practice and what provides the sort of life that I want for myself in future.

I can speak from the professional experience of treating over a thousand inpatients at PROMIS for their eating disorders but I think it would be more helpful if I were to speak now solely from my own personal experience of having an eating disorder. I have had to be prepared to put my ideas into practice in my own life. Not only that, I risk my future professional security by employing former patients. I wonder how many other treatment directors in psychological or psychiatric treatment programmes are prepared to do that.

For myself, my weight no longer varies appreciably whereas previously it used to vary up and down within a range of 50 lbs once or even twice a year. I was forever on diets and forever beating myself up because of their failure. I was at war with my tailor because my suits would never fit between successive appointments for measurement. I kept different sizes of shirt in my wardrobe. I once lost thirty pounds in weight in three weeks and believed it to be a triumph. My secretary told me that patients thought I must have a dreadful illness. They were right: an eating disorder is a dreadful illness and it has a high morbidity and mortality rate. On another occasion our other secretary complained that I had eaten her lunch - I was helping myself to odd nibbles from the fridge in between seeing patients and had not realised that her lunch had been devoured as I moved from left to right through all the contents of the fridge. My wife despaired of my eating habits, never knowing what I would like or dislike, accept or reject. All I wanted was to grab whatever was available NOW with the intolerance of any addict.

Nowadays I eat for pleasure. I enjoy my meals. I don't scoff them at speed. I like the taste and the texture. I know what it is to feel hungry - which I never knew before because I never allowed it to happen. I know what it is to feel the whole range of my human feelings - because I don't stuff them down with food or with other addictive substances or processes. I take time to do the things that I enjoy: I am no longer driven like a mad thing. I have the things that I most want:

i.   Peace of mind in spite of unsolved problems - and I have plenty of them, particularly economically and professionally, mostly of my own causing.

ii.   I have a happy, mutually fulfilling relationship, with my wife and with most of my family and staff (perfection is impossible) and also with a wide range of friends.

iii. I have all the joys of experiencing spontaneity, creativity and enthusiasm. I have a wide range of personal interests, mostly in literature, theatre, opera and ballet.

I have considerable privilege in my personal and professional life. I am well paid as a doctor and I have an immensely supportive and patient wife. All this is a very long way from the wretched creature I was twenty years ago in the side ward of a mental nursing home. In many ways some of the challenges that I have today are greater than they were at that time, but I am better able to deal with them. I work the Twelve Step programme because it works for me. On that personal experience I recommend it to others.

Appendix
PROMIS Eating Disorder Guidelines

What is Abstinence?

It is important not to make food, and the behaviours around it, the central issue in recovery from an eating disorder. Abstinence from compulsive overeating, starving, vomiting and purging is only the first step and not the ultimate goal in itself.

The whole purpose of recovery from addictive disease is to be able to rid ourselves of emotional obsessions and their damaging physical consequences. Simply changing an obsession for doing something into an obsession for not doing something (for example going from bingeing into starving or *vice versa*) is no improvement. The correct treatment for both is to follow these guidelines for abstinence - in order to relieve the physical consequences of addictive behaviour - and then work the Twelve Step programme in order to facilitate long-term emotional and psychological health. Many people come into Twelve Step recovery programmes after years of disordered eating patterns. These guidelines are an attempt to answer some of their questions on how to be physically abstinent from using food addictively.

The basic issues of abstinence in an eating disorder are simple and straightforward, just as simple as for alcohol or drugs: put down the addictive substances and behaviours, then experience and deal appropriately with the feelings that arise and learn to cope with the various realities of life.

These guidelines are useful for patients in early recovery when we may have little or no concept of how to fuel their bodies healthily. They are a framework - not a diet or strict regime - around which we can build a long-term, well-balanced and healthy way of eating.

The Twelve Step principle concerning addictive substances is one of total abstinence. We are powerless over mood-altering foods (sugar and other refined carbohydrates) and we need to be totally abstinent from them, just as alcoholics avoid alcohol entirely. Food of some kind is essential for life but refined carbohydrates are not. Nor is alcohol. Compulsive overeaters often make out that they have a particularly challenging time because they confront food every day - but they are wrong: alcoholics have to drink something every day in order to stay alive, just as sufferers from eating disorders have to eat. However, alcoholics do not have to drink mood-altering drinks (anything that contains alcohol) and, correspondingly, eating disorder sufferers do not have to eat specific foods that have a mood-altering effect, nor do they have to involve themselves in mood-altering behaviours around food. Abstinence is possible just as straightforwardly for people with eating disorders as it is for alcoholics.

We have to have a clear definition of our abstinence. We need to avoid those food substances - the refined carbohydrates (sugar and white flour) - that are more likely to lead us back to using food obsessively or compulsively. Behavioural abstinence involves having three regular meals daily with nothing to eat in between. Chewing stimulates the appetite centre of the brain. Once stimulated, it remains "turned on" for about twenty minutes. Grazing between meals can therefore result in a constant feeling of hunger or expectation of food. For the same reason it is possible still to feel hungry after a vast, but rapid, binge.

General Information

Eating should be a pleasure: the taste and process of eating should be enjoyable.

Fluid retention, diabetes, thyroid deficiency and various other medical conditions can have an effect on body weight but can easily be controlled medically and should have no effect on the simultaneous treatment of an eating disorder.

As a general rule for good health, one should drink one and a half to two litres (seven to ten cups) of fluid each day.

Bottled sauces are best avoided because many of them contain sugar or white flour or they may be very spicy and stimulate the appetite. They may also blunt the palate so that it becomes progressively less sensitive to delicate flavouring.

Appetite suppressants should be totally avoided because they are addictive. It should be realised that nicotine, caffeine and diet drinks tend to be used as appetite suppressants. These substances are, in any case, addictive in their own right – whatever the reason for their use.

Laxatives should be avoided because they form part of the binge/purge behavioural addiction component of an eating disorder. Bowel function takes time to return to normal after years of abuse through an eating disorder. Patients with anorexia, for example, will often complain that they are "constipated" when what they mean is that they have the sensation of something in their bowels. This sensation is therefore not due to constipation but to hypersensitivity as a result of years of starvation.

Taking regular exercise is healthy but as little as twenty or thirty minutes a day for three days a week is quite healthy enough. Exercise and the "high" it can produce can become an addiction in itself.

It takes about ten days for the emotional high and subsequent withdrawal symptoms from sugar to clear. Each sugar binge will result in its own withdrawal period.

If you experience any craving to binge, purge or starve you should share these feelings with someone at the time, if this is possible. Cravings are not something to be ashamed about. Nor are they a sign that things are going badly. Indeed, they are entirely normal and they are common for an addict in early recovery.

So-called "forbidden foods", particularly in anorexic patients, tend to become an obsession. These patients often make lists of forbidden foods - usually fats, meats and wholegrain carbohydrates - that are all perfectly healthy. This obsession can even sometimes take the form of supposed food allergies and tactical vegetarianism (designed to produce weight loss, rather than from philosophical conviction). When we come into recovery it is important to reconsider what we are prepared to eat.

Meal times should be as regular as possible. Some sufferers find excuses to have breakfast at 5am or put dinner off until 11pm. We need to learn to keep within normal timetables, such as having breakfast at 7 - 9am, lunch at 12 - 2pm and dinner at 7 - 9pm. These are guidelines only and may not suit shift work. However, it is important to have three meals well spaced throughout the working hours.

Bulimic patients should avoid using the lavatory for at least one hour after each meal and they should try to remain in the company of other people rather than isolate themselves at those times. Meal times in early recovery are likely to be vulnerable and uncomfortable times and it is therefore a good idea to talk about feelings at these times.

Anorexic patients should eat with other people at regular times and allow themselves to be seen to be eating.

The quantity that we should eat at any time should be determined by physical hunger, the same as for other people, rather than by the need to satisfy or suppress emotional cravings in one way or another. Food is a fuel for the body, comparable to putting petrol into the tank of a car.

A normal quantity of food is easily determined by recognising whether we would be perfectly happy to exchange our own plate of food for that of someone else who does not have an eating disorder. If the prospect of doing so fills us with fear - that we will have either too little or too much - then our perceptions are still being ruled by our addictive disease. Second helpings should be avoided.

The total quantity of food that we require in any one day is that which enables body weight to remain constant without continually thinking about it and without using exercise, laxatives, diuretics, strict control of food intake and various purgative processes as control mechanisms for body weight.

In the early days of abstinence some guidance may be useful on the concept of normal eating, but making out particular "food plans" or having "food sponsors" can be dangerously obsessive. It gives food a power that it does not possess. There is no need to count out exact weights, portions or calories. We need to learn to eat according to genuine physical hunger rather than emotional cravings.

Body Image
The approximate ideal body weight or goal weight for someone suffering from an eating disorder can easily be determined from medical charts, even though those charts tend to under-estimate the range of healthy weight for a particular height or body frame. It is not determined by fashion, or by any individual patient's feelings of what he or she ought to look like, feel like or fit into. Recovery is about getting away from trying to control our feelings through our addictive relationship with food and exercise and through changing our physical appearance.

We do not need even to talk about food or body weight. Body weight will vary a few pounds on a day-to-day basis in any case, according to body fluid content. Attempting to control one's exact body weight or body image, and the constant weighing of both food and self, is part of the obsession of an eating disorder, often handing emotional power over to what the scales say that day - or even several times a day. As long as we are abstinent, there should be no real need to weigh ourselves more than once a month - at most - as an occasional check. Actuarial tables for normal height and weight (for life insurance purposes) give a range of five to ten pounds for each height and frame. It is important to get away from the concept of an 'excess' five pounds which 'makes all the difference' to how we feel about ourselves. Initially it may be an excellent idea for us to throw out the bathroom scales and possibly hand over the occasional check on our weight to a trusted friend or partner who can then tell us whether we are still within the healthy range, even though not telling us our exact weight. This practice should not need to be continued in the long term. As a general principle, if our clothes still fit in the same way that they did when we reached our goal weight, then there is no need for us to weigh ourselves any more.

Body image is an exceedingly complex subject. Naturally we want to look and feel good, but this is often a decision on what we feel we *ought* to look like in terms of body shape, clothing and fashion. These are emotional concepts rather than physical absolutes. Patients with eating disorders tend to have a distorted body image so that a sufferer from anorexia will perceive himself or herself as being fatter than anyone else would perceive. Correspondingly, a compulsive overeater might see himself or herself as much thinner than reality and a sufferer from bulimia may have a very narrow range of body weight or shape that he or she would perceive as "normal".

Perhaps the most difficult aspect of receiving help for an eating disorder is, as with any other addiction, coming to see that one's own concepts may be passionately held but may nonetheless be deluded.

No Sugar and White Flour
Sufferers from eating disorders have particular sensitivity to refined carbohydrates. For them, sugar and white flour of any kind, where the fibre roughage has been purified away, lead to a chemical reaction within the brain, producing an emotional lift and setting up a physical and emotional craving. This is one of the reasons that, in these people, eating one chocolate leads on to devouring the whole box, and why we often crave for things such as pastries, cakes or sweets. This craving is exactly similar to the craving for alcohol set up by the first use in any day of alcohol in sufferers from alcoholism, or the cravings set up by the first use in any day of any other mood-altering substance or process. In each case it is the first use in any day that does the damage. This is the origin of the saying in Alcoholics Anonymous that one glass is too much and a barrel too little, or for the warning in Overeaters Anonymous that we should beware of the first *compulsive* bite. It also explains the humorous new word "ufluation": checking in the refrigerator to see if something has mysteriously appeared in the ten minutes since we last looked.

Appropriate physical abstinence, which avoids all sugar, including honey and syrups and all refined carbohydrates of any kind, dramatically reduces the likelihood of craving or bingeing. On the whole, other foods should be confronted just as an alcoholic would confront milk or orange juice: with no problem whatever.

Some sufferers from eating disorders get themselves into a habit of using specific "binge foods" such as fats or fruit or almost anything. This is just a habit that can be broken once the cravings are no longer stimulated by sugar and refined carbohydrates. Sufferers from anorexia should be abstinent from sugar and refined carbohydrates, even though they are high-calorie foods, because they stimulate the cravings that they fear will never stop. Once anorexic patients are abstinent from these substances, they can learn to trust food again.

Artificial sweeteners are the equivalent of non-alcoholic beer for alcoholic patients: they keep the sense of taste attuned to what we used to like. The risk of artificial sweeteners is the same as the risk of alcohol-free beer: sooner or later we crave the real thing. Many eating disorder sufferers have well-developed addictive relationships with diet drinks and sugar-free gums. These have to be avoided. Similarly, adding salt and pepper and various spices and bottled sauces to our food will tend to stimulate the appetite excessively and keep our taste buds over-stimulated. It is best to avoid these substances altogether as additives and allow ourselves to develop a sense of taste for the more subtle flavours in food. Sufferers from eating disorders tend to like to eat stronger, sweeter, saltier, spicier foods than most people and therefore it can take several months for our taste buds to get used to normal flavours.

MSG (monosodium glutamate) is often present in Chinese and Indian food and is best avoided, as it is a general sweetener and preservative. We need to retrain our palates to enjoy foods that are less sweet. In recovery we soon learn how to choose dishes in a Chinese or Indian restaurant or elsewhere that do not contain MSG.

If a label has a sugar listed in fifth place or lower in the list of ingredients then the traces can be considered to be negligible. However, this is just a general observation and we should initially avoid *any* substance that makes us crave, irrespective of its position on the label, although we should be careful of becoming - or remaining - obsessive on this point.

White or brown sugar, sucrose, maltose, lactose, glucose, dextrose, caramel, honey, malt, molasses, cane or corn syrup, sorbitol, manitol, saccharin and aspartate should all be avoided.

For carbohydrates it is easier to list the safe carbohydrates: wholemeal bread, whole-wheat grain crackers, whole-wheat pasta, unrefined rice, wholegrain cereals and potatoes. Watch out for "wheat flour" that is refined and often present in sauces as a thickening agent, although wheat itself is no risk. Brown bread may be white bread, made from refined flour that has been stained brown. Only wholemeal bread is safe. Wheat flour itself in its unrefined form in bread is perfectly safe. It is the refining process, not the particular grain, that causes the cravings.

Summary of an Abstinent Day
Eat three meals - breakfast, lunch and dinner - every day.

When travelling inter-continental distances by air, have four meals on the long days and two on the short days.

Eat nothing at all in between meals.

Avoid all white flour and other refined carbohydrates.

Avoid all sugars and artificial sweeteners.

Avoid all alcohol because alcohol is itself a refined carbohydrate and sets up cravings for others.

Do not carry around bottled water. Anorexic patients do this so that they can readily suppress cravings. It is a fad that should be avoided.

Keep to a total of one glass of fruit juice a day.

Patients needing to gain some weight may be advised to have a couple of "build-up", high- calorie drinks in the course of the day. This should be discussed with a counsellor.

A normal healthy diet should comprise daily intake from each of three principal food groups:

a) Fats: milk, butter, cheese, and oils.
b) Carbohydrates: bread, cereals, pasta, grains, fresh fruit and vegetables.
c) Proteins: meat, fish, eggs, cheese, pulses, tofu, soya, nuts and yoghurt.

The *exact* composition of a sensible diet, with a range of fats, carbohydrates and proteins is not of any great interest to people in recovery from eating disorders. Healthy eating is simply a matter of having a well-balanced food intake, exactly the same balance as for anything else in life. Sufferers from eating disorders do not need to be told anything elaborate about balance, because it can become obsessive. However, we may need basic information in the early days of our recovery. The food chart illustrated below is a good general guide on how an average day's food intake may be constructed, clearly indicating the importance of carbohydrates as an energy provider.

An average breakfast may consist of a portion of porridge or cereal followed by an egg or other protein and a slice of whole-wheat toast with butter and sugar-free marmalade. Lunch and dinner should consist of a balanced plate of food roughly split into three selections from the three main food groups and followed by a sugar-free pudding or a piece of fruit or cheese. The healthiest way to measure one's food, as already mentioned, is not to weigh it but to check whether one could comfortably exchange plates with a normal eater.

Daily food balance
fats and oils : Use sparingly.
milk, yoghurt and cheese: 2 - 3 servings.
meat, poultry, fish, beans, eggs, nuts: 2 - 3 servings.
fruits : 2 - 4 servings.
vegetables: 3 - 5 servings.
bread, cereal, rice, wholemeal pasta: 6 - 10 servings.

(The number of "servings" is not a precise quantity to be consumed - which is determined by maintenance of healthy body weight - but illustrates the approximate healthy ratio between one food group and another.)

Other books in the series

Preventing Addiction

Cigarette Smoking. Fifteen reasons for continuing to smoke (or not)

Healing

Dangerous Doctors

Spiritual Awakening. Working the Twelve Step programme

Inside the Madness

How to Combat Alcoholism and Addiction

How to Combat Anorexia, Bulimia and Compulsive Overeating

Spirituality for Atheists and Agnostics

A New Life. Healing depression

Compulsive Helping

Healthy Relationships

Prescription Drug Addiction. My doctor gave it to me

Behavioural Addictions: Workaholism. Shopaholism. Exercise Addiction. Gambling and Risk Taking. Self-Harming. Obsessive Compulsive Disorder

False Medical Gods

Detoxification and Harm Minimisation

Childhood Abuse and Abandonment

Healing Emotional Trauma with E.M.D.R.

Healing Emotional Trauma with Psychodrama

Treating Chronic Relapse. Not again

Help: The Dairy of a Private Doctor

    Vol 1: I will *not* make do. The philosophy and politics of help

    Vol 2: Daughters are Difficult. Professional help in clinical practice

    Vol 3: Henry is a Good Man. The boundaries of help

    Vol 4: Robin's turn. Beyond help